ROMANCE, KALIK, AND CONCH SALAD

Things Bahamian

By

George Major

ISBN: 1-40332-795-5

This book is printed on acid free paper.

1st Books - rev. 04/25/02

Contents

ROMANCE 1

Romance, The Tropics and Conch Salad 2
Love's Beautiful Stranger 112
Detached in Mother's care 127

ISLAND LIFE 129

Jabim 130
Living on the Edge of the World 137
The Beauty of Abaco Built 139
Has Paradise lost? The Future of Eleuthera Island
in the Bahamas 140
In the Blessed Moments of Morning 151
Scenes of a Daily Fish Market 157
Everything is Poetry, They Say 160
Inquiry and Knowledge 169
The Golden Rays of Sunshine 172
A Week in the Life of an Island Man 179
Tourist Beauty 182
The Old Trickster 187
Sweet nature's answers to the tyranny of village life
.... 193
A Writer Confesses 200

Introspection 205

This Journey's Too Sweet to Miss 206
Fears of our Fathers 216
Streams of gold 217

Quelled into contentment 223
Fascination 225
All is Quiet on the Western Front 226
Out of nothing comes nothing 232
Operating Velocity 240
Heavy Drifts 243
Why God Made Me a Poet 246
My Sense of Purpose 248

Dreams 254

For Brittany 255
Charlie, the Internet and Bob Marley 257

ROMANCE

George Major

Romance, The Tropics and Conch Salad

Nestled among the archipelago of the Bahamian Islands, Eleuthera stands out as a most beautiful, private destination where one can experience the native lifestyle, cuisine and tropical splendor. If you are looking for a truly exotic destination this may be the ideal place for you.

I gave a gorgeous California girl two beautiful weeks of sun, fun and romance in the Bahamas. We had a really wonderful time touring my island together. Our lovely tour of Eleuthera Island was both memorable and special; an experience we will treasure for a lifetime.

I met Angela through an Internet classified personal dating service. At first it was an obscure relationship, but as soon as she realized that I was genuinely interested in love she gave in. We really got to know and trust each other intimately through our many phone calls and emails, and I became her best friend and love. We chatted by telephone and online for several months using programs like ICQ, AOL Instant Messenger and Microsoft outlook. After becoming attached to Angela and feeling the need to have her as a part of my life, I proposed a romantic two-week vacation for her to my home, Eleuthera Island, in the Bahamas.

I went to a local travel agency, made the arrangements and sent the ticket information via computer to Los Angeles, California. Thanks to the Internet and telephone, we kept in close contact every single day, especially up to the last few days before her arrival. Many promises and innuendoes were made so we both knew and were prepared for the possibilities — or so we thought. In retrospect, love is more real and passionate up close and personal, and most importantly live.

Angela had never traveled so far away from home or outside the United States before, but she would take the chance of her lifetime and find the love she so badly wanted. She trusted me and knew that I would be the gracious host I had promised to be. She had seen my photos and had talked to me enough to be assured that I was someone she could take the chance of her lifetime with. And so she would leap on a flight destined for the Island of Eleuthera, Bahamas and have the time of her life basking beneath the warm golden sun and reveling in the gracious hospitality of Eleuthera Islanders, especially myself. A journey into a world she had only imagined before.

The possibility that she would actually spend time here was exciting enough, but like millions of other Americans, she might have decided never to return home. This experience would enlighten her and expand her horizons. What better send-off into her new life at a California college?

We had the best time on the island of Eleuthera. Every beach we went to was secluded, no one else in sight for miles. We were not bothered and therefore free to explore love and excite ourselves with this beauty and splendor at our disposal. Each day we did things that were new and exciting to both of us. I even rediscovered my island paradise and got a sense of what the tourists see when they flock to our shores. I realized that it is quite beautiful and untouched still, as unique and charming as always. It really has very beautiful spots that are capable of enchanting someone for a long or short visit.

There are a few mystiques, like pink sand, a popular mythical notion that really does exist in several locations on Eleuthera Island. Bits and pieces of broken pink seashells mix with the white, shining powder of the sand. The end product is the most memorable sight, and one of many reasons that millions of tourists around the world come to our islands.

After a splendid week of touring and beaching we moved on to Nassau where we had our best personal time. Nassau is quite nice but not as free and natural as the grand Eleuthera landscape, although in Nassau there are more tourist sights, tours and organized entertainment. I took my jeep along on the trip and was able to show my love the whole island including some more unique and local places that tourists don't often get a chance to see.

Angela met members of my family both in Eleuthera and Nassau; she had a chance to see places like the fantastic tourist sites of Peanuts Taylor's Drum Beat Club, the Atlantis Resort, Paradise Island and Crystal Cay Marine Park, The Cable Beach Casino, the traditional Straw Market of West Bay Street and much more.

We had lots of romance and fun along the way. I can tell you a bit more if you come along…

Chapter one

Monday the 06th of August
Her Arrival

After knowing Angela for sometime, getting to know her personality and the fact that she was an enjoyable person to be around I felt compelled to be close to her. It had been sometime since I had meaningful female companionship and I was happy that this beautiful specimen of a female had chosen to spend some time with me vacationing in Eleuthera, Bahamas, my home. I was dizzy with the thought that she would be here in a few moments. Soon her plane from Miami would arrive. I would have someone special near me. Someone that I would have all to myself, I'm selfish sometimes and like to have things my own way when I can. This, I thought, would be the perfect platform and format to be in. She would be here with me. I would take care of her, love her and she would be all mine. It was like a dream come true. I couldn't wait to see what fantasy my beautiful California girl would bring into my life. I found Angela to be very honest in everything she said and found that she was well protected and close to her family, who were worried about her going on such a long journey; so far away from home with some mystery man whom they had never met. She however was excited with the notion of visiting. She needed a vacation; after all of her college studies had just been completed and she was in the process of searching for a new job, a vacation with her new friend would be just the antidote for her situation. She felt enchanted at the idea of someone inviting her on such an elaborate and well-planned vacation. She, Angela, had never traveled outside of California and had never flown in an aircraft before. In her excitement to see the Bahamas she threw caution to the wind. After she received her airline tickets she waited patiently until August 6th when the Los Angeles airport reopened from a phase of construction. That day she would be driven to the airport and take off in a large jet scheduled to go through Salt Lake city to Atlanta Georgia, on to Miami then finally landing in beautiful Governors harbor, Eleuthera, Bahamas the following day at noon. She would fly all night thinking and unafraid. Dreaming only of meeting me and feeling for herself the excitement of air travel and the excitement of a preplanned exciting rendezvous with a handsome Bahamian man who was as excited as she was about meeting someone new and sharing further our love for each other.

The phones rang often, we chatted in text and voice through Instant messenger programs, Paltalk wasn't on the market yet, the computers sent email daily as I encouraged Angela and removed all doubt; that there would be no problem while she was on vacation with me. I assured her that I would take great care of her and make each day enjoyable and exciting. I knew she felt the excitement as well since she called and emailed me often alerting me to her level of excitement. Getting out of Los Angeles for a while was for her a great prospect at the time. Some friends were giving her problems and a few weeks in the Bahamas would give her a chance to rest from all of this nonsense for a while and probably give her problems in California a chance to go away by the time she got back into town two weeks later. She would shop when she could and gather the necessary oils and aids she needed to be comfortable in our climate down here. From the beginning she insisted that her accommodations have air-conditioning so that she would be able to beat the summer heat I described to her, not knowing that the heat was dryer and worst in Los Angeles where she lived. She had applied for a few jobs in town and hoped that by the time she got back from her great vacation she would have a positive offer to consider, everything came up roses.

She went for it and noon of the 6th of August I was on the tarmac at the Governors International Airport to meet the flight. American eagle assured me that she would make their 3pm flight out of Miami after the fact that she missed the earlier flight at noon. I sat at the airport and waited feeling lonely and dejected thinking that perhaps she really did not come or had changed her mind making a fool out of me in the process. For two whole hours I waited in the cafe having popcorn and lemonade while my Los Angeles girl made her way out of Miami on the three o'clock flight. I thought in my mind that if she did not come there was a good reason, like she got a sudden fear of flying and did not come or she decided not to take the chance of a distant vacation with her new found handsome man after all. I hoped for the best and was quite happy when I saw the medium blonde in the white and blue flowered vest walking toward the terminal to clear Bahamas customs. I looked in through the windows and waved to a somewhat weary looking traveler as she waved back in a slow non-energetic manner. I wondered if she would be instantly happy or if she would be a bit shy, how would she adjust? She had not shown any adverse signs up to this point so I felt relieved. She had been bubbly and assured me that she at 34 she was a confident woman who could take care of herself. I felt confident with that and knew that I would have less of a job on my hands taking care of her.

With her state of mind we would truly have a good time in each others company since I was happy and charged with energy and she was feeling the same way nothing but good could come out of all of this. Finally she checked out of customs and came out to meet me with a humble greeting and a big hug and kiss from me, how divine. I held her for a moment in the company of the taxi drivers looking on and felt quite good that she had accepted my friendly gestures of affection and moved on assisting her with the baggage to the jeep for the joyful conversative ride to beautiful Hiltons Haven in Tarpum Bay. Once inside the jeep we exchanged pleasantries. She explained that she was quite tired since she had been traveling from 6pm the evening before until now 3pm today. She was tired and full of jet lag and needed to be taken to the hotel for some bed rest before resuming any activities. I considered this to be fine and knew that it gave me some extra time to think about her comfort and further plan the evening ahead of us. She seemed quite relaxed and open to our friendship as she has before over the phone so I felt quite comfortable and relaxed in her company. I felt I knew her well and expected nothing out of the ordinary. She was beautiful, her bright blue eyes under her rimmed designer glasses, dressed simply in her flowered blue vest with jeans and appropriate walking shoes. She was down to earth in conversation and quite bright as she looked at me smiling when she could to reassure me that she was happy that I was there. She reassured me as she did before that she was like a little kid and she was entirely in my care to take care of and guide her, teaching her everything she needed to know in her new environment. I felt fine with that. I felt the tenderness she assumed and her warmth of heart was evident.

We arrived at the Hiltons Haven Motel thirty minutes later. I ushered Angela to her room, delivered her luggage and left her alone to regroup herself and rest from her long exhausting journey by air. After a rest at the motel, Hiltons Haven in Tarpum Bay, I took Angela to my office telephone in order for her to call home and assure her family that she had arrived safely and that she was all right. She gave them the information they needed to know to make them comfortable with her new surroundings in order to relieve her of the worry of them. Her teenage children had been placed with friends and family appropriately so that they would be comfortable and she told me that her seven year old was living with his father's new family in Michigan so everyone was appropriately placed and there would be no worry on either side. I found out a few days later that she worried a bit.

Angela had changed to some relaxing duds quite appropriate to the island and quite enticing. Her untanned white skin shone brightly in the daylight and she looked delicious and delectable. She had pinned her hair up to avoid the heat of the sun and was quite relieved with the air-conditioning both in the van and in the room which she was placed in by the motel owner. After her resting awhile and making the phone calls she was finally ready to sit back in the jeep and take a ride that I had planned for her. I had gone over this scenario several times in my mind and hoped that everything would go according to plan. I knew the task at hand; I only had to take the necessary time to choose the appropriate event to fill the correct moment. I felt with Angela's relaxed attitude and attentiveness this would be done. She was relaxed as a pup ready to experience the goodness of Eleuthera Island, which she had briefly seen on her long scenic drive from the airport. She had mostly seen the beautiful Caribbean Sea and the greenery of the island so far. We had passed through several settlements (villages) to get from the airport at Governors Harbor to Hiltons Haven in Tarpum Bay. She had seen the settlements of Governors Harbor, Palmetto Point, Savannah Sound and Tarpum Bay quite briefly and only in passing. I would take my time while she was here and show her those villages and more in closer more delightful detail. We would be dining out and having a great time when and wherever we could so there was no rush for anything only the need to relax and enjoy it all. I would enjoy my Eleuthera Island all over again as well.

I had taken these two weeks off from work. I closed my business for a two-week vacation while Angela was here and I would reopen only after she was happily back in the Unite States and Los Angeles; after her having the most beautiful loving time of her life. I promised to give it my all to make her feel happy and to make her mine while she enjoyed our island and country and beyond. So off we went at 4:30pm in the afternoon that Monday on a tour of Tarpum Bay, my hometown, the most beautiful place on earth. Tarpum Bay is an average sized waterfront Bahamian fishing village with a nice village charm. I was sure that Angela would like Tarpum Bay since all of the visitors whom I had ever met said that they loved Tarpum Bay best among the islands villages; because they said, primarily the friendliness of its people and its open outlay along the open turquoise Caribbean seashore. The view from the waterfront Baystreet in Tarpum Bay is a view of the remainder of the Northern Island landscape; of the remainder of the island which curves along the horizon from Tarpum Bay forty miles away to Governors Harbor which is also on the Caribbean Seashore and is quite equally attractive as well since it has such nice people and the attractiveness of the seashore. Tarpum Bay was resting during that time of the afternoon, the streets were empty in the midday heat and not many people were visible at the time. Later that day they would return to the streets to playfully complete their chores and make the errands their parents needed to have done that day. Later town would be abuzz with a labyrinth like ants making traffic throughout the town. For now Angela saw the quiet beauty of the town and took it in quietly as we drove through on our way to having an early dinner at North Side resort in the settlement of RockSound, which is eight miles to the South of Tarpum Bay.

We would drive for another eight miles through the lush greenery along the winding roads to North Side where we would be fed a sumptuous Bahamian dinner prepared by the main cook Allison with much experience in making guest happy at meal time. I was making sure that this day would be the best and that Angela from this day on would fall in love with the island. I wanted to make her as comfortable as one of us Eleuthera Islanders and show her that I truly did want to love her and make her happy. This I truly wanted to do and she was just beginning to actually see this. The drive to Rock Sound was fairly uneventful. I pointed out the farm, Chris farm where they raised cattle that produced quite exquisite Swiss Chalet beef and luscious Eleuthera Papaya, which is exported into Texas and other destinations. I pointed out the island power station where so many friends worked and the airport across the street from the plant when many local flights came in and the elite of Cotton Bay and the south landed their private Jets from around the world and worked hard with us to keep our dreams of a vital rich economy alive. We went on to the main part of town through to the intersection, which led to North Side resort. Once we arrived we met only the Chef and a few workers there. We literally had the whole compound and the North side beach to our selves. Right away we ordered some delicious platters to eat and headed off to give Angela her first glimpse of our pink sand and the beauty of the Eleuthera Island Beach. Here was the first time I held her warm hand and came close to her alerting her that my love was on the prowl and I was searching and in need of some of her warmth. My warm peck on her cheek let her know that I was here for her whenever needed me but for now we needed some more good times to bring us closer together and some good food to keep us happy and focused on making this loving time a success for us both.

Angela did enjoy the pink sandy beaches of North Side just before dinner and began to collect her first sample of shells of which I assured her there were plenty and there was no rush to collect as I know where the best places were for shelling on the other side of the island. She gazed at me deeply with a nice smile with her deep blue eyes and reassured me that she was enjoying every moment equally as much or more than I was.

The meal was delicious. Allison had fixed for Angela a combination seafood platter, which included for her this now famous sea snail conch. I told her before that conch was a great aphrodisiac hinting that it was just for lovers such as we were, that conch was the food of those seeking to have good love relations including many cozy hours cuddling and enjoying prolonged, pleasurable, coitious. She did enjoy the conch and implications it carried with it. I enjoyed my grouper fingers with peas and rice which went so well with the gravy and the cold wry taste of a tall Kalik beer which is the nations favorite beer and the only one I would introduce to any visitor to the island. Kalik with almost any dish including seafood is simply delicious, Angela agreed with me. This was a new cuisine for Angela but she enjoyed it and said later after a course of conch fritters and dip that it was very good for her to have experienced it. She felt quite enchanted after the meal. We said good-bye to Allison and set off for a nice after dinner drive around 8pm back to Hiltons Haven in Tarpum Bay. Tonight would be an early night. I would not stay out late with

Angela. I would allow her to get lots of rest tonight to overcome the jetlag she had experienced. I wanted her rested and comfortable for the next days adventure and my loving advances, which I felt coming on by the moment, Angela was really open and nice to be around.

Chapter two

Tuesday 07th of August
Grand touring North

The following day I had a day trip to the magical island of Harbor Island planned. Once there we would experience some of the magic this island produces. This island is different it is warm and it is charming, the people are nice and homey, the clubs are hopping and the food is great. It's a fantastic combination of island life meets metropolitan. Its great to just be apart of it all. In Harbor Island there are numerous tourist locations, hotels like the Run away hill or the Pink Sands. Just fantastic places you can relax and enjoy the broad surf beach, run in for a swim at any time or just lay in the sun and get that great tan you always dreamed about. Angela had talked about catching a tan so this would be the place for her to do so. She had already started to tan and she looked great with a darker hue of which she was attentive to and quite delighted to have. All was a go. Oh, the conch salad from the stall by the seashore in Harbor Island is the best in the world. It's the best and the freshest I have ever had. They take the conch directly from the shell and process it for the salad right there while you watch. Its fantastic. You can watch the whole process and enjoy the rich experience of the rich vital salad being prepared right before your eyes, all for $5.00. The salad is a concoction of finely sliced conch combined with a variety of juicy vegetable salad items like Onion, green peppers, tomatoes, Lime juice, salt and hot goat pepper if you wish. We did enjoy our Salads.

The intake of these salads in addition to being an Island aphrodisiac is an energy giving experience. The fresh, tart salad enlivens the palette leaving the mouth watering from the combination of delightful vegetable contents. We took some great photos of the lady making the salad as well.

Our morning trip to Harbor Island began at 9am. I drove to the motel where Angela was up and ready to receive me. She was fresh in her bikini; jean shorts covered her. She wore the appropriate silver slippers for the occasion. She looked so appealing. She wore her hair down that day I remember. We had a long drive from Tarpum Bay to Harbor Island. The road trip is some 100 miles of roadway, mostly scenic driving. I love to drive anytime so it's no problem for me. I was especially charged anyway so it was a joy to take the hour and a half it would take to make our way up the scenic island to enjoy the day in Beautiful Harbor Island. After passing through the settlement of James Cistern and the big rock grocery store we came upon," the cliffs." A road sign indicated the location of this popular, unusual landscape. These Cliffs are a fantastic natural spectacular scene, which serve good as a memory of Eleuthera Island. The stunning feature of the Cliffs are their height and the color of the deep blue ocean, the Atlantic, which washes the face of the these cliffs producing a bright white foam which when combined with the other elements creates a very memorable view which must be seen when visiting tourist sites in Eleuthera. Angela and I spent about twenty minutes at the face of the Cliffs carefully crawling around and enjoying the spectacular view, taking photographs at every opportunity. After this fun experience we set off again along Queens Highway at a snails pace attempting to take it all in as we went up the island.

The next stunning view was seen as we approached Hatchet Bay, a once great producer of world proportion in the Pineapple Industry during the 1800s and a National producer of livestock and dairy products during the early 1900s. Sad to say it I s now a bygone era for Hatchet Bay but the monuments of her past glory still stand. The many Grain elevators, which served the livestock industry there, still stand towering over the landscape looking like something out of a science fiction novel. Our present population hasn't a clue of the use of such machinery (structures) or why they came to be sitting near the highway in the vast green unoccupied fields of sweet green grass once occupied by exotic breeds of dairy and beef cattle. I have passed this way so many times and admired these structures and dreamed of reviving this industry solely for the glory of Eleuthera. We then moved on.

We passed through several towns enjoying the view until we came upon Gregory town. Gregory Town is the home of the famous annual Pineapple festival. Thousands of tourists and Bahamians gather in June to this entertaining event. In the center of Gregory town Angela spotted several gift shops, stores that sold authentic Bahamian artifacts and T-shirts especially for the tourist to enjoy. We stopped at," Island made", a store owned by Mrs. Thompson, which has been around for sometime. Her gift shop has the look and charm to please the customer. There Angela found a few anklets, a few T-shirts and I found to my surprise several books written by two wonderful

Bahamian authors whom I am always ready and willing to read. Cheryl Albury and Michael Pintards books of poetry and short stories were new to me. I hoped to find interesting material in these books and hopefully find the time to read during the idle time within the coming weeks. I hoped there would be time to enjoy some Bahamian literature. I have always been curious about writing and wanted the opportunity to digest the offerings of these brave new Bahamian authors.

We had a brief chat with Mrs. Thompson and came to agreement on the works a few local artists that we both knew. One of who advertised some of his work in her store, the locally renowned painter Kevin Cooper. An artist with a great passion for the craft not unlike many of the great masters of our time, Brent Malone, Mr. Kendrick Knowles and so on. Mrs. Thompson wished us well and sent us on our way with great enthusiasm and news that we certainly would enjoy our day trip to Harbor Island. She pointed out some particularly good restaurants there many of which I didn't know and didn't remember by the time I got there. Angela told me one of her duties while being here, She was charged by her mother to collect as proof or souvenir some of this much talked about pink sand that we have here. Harbor Island has the most beautiful pink sand. I truly feel that Harbor island has the best beaches I have ever seen in all the places I have seen in the world, the wide, clean pink sandy beaches are truly stunning. Their location on the eastern shore bordering the deep navy blue and turquoise shallows of the Atlantic Ocean are quite a spectacular and stunning view to take in. The pinkness in the sand brought about by the tiny bits of red coral gathered with the white sand is spectacular. Angela got her chance to collect her mother's gift. I told her while we were there that I truly felt that I was in Paradise, we were having such a great time together. Our trip to the pink Sands beach topped it all off and brought heaven a little closer to home.

So on we went from Gregory town toward Harbor Island along the Queens highway, which runs the entire 120 miles of the island and is the only main road on the island. Its long winding appearance, narrow in some places is in itself a unique experience of Eleuthera Island. The Queens highway, a winding path with a thin black top, relatively smooth with very few hills winds its way for 120 miles from the Northern most," Spanish Wells", to the southern most Lighthouse beach at Bannerman town, Eleuthera. The glass windows bridge was the next stop for us on our journey north to our day in Harbor Island. This site similar to the Cliffs at James Cistern, which we visited earlier, is more stunning. The stunning and most outstanding feature of the glass windows bridge is the contrast of the water on both sides of the bridge where the island breaks in two halves; the only place to do so and is the narrowest passage on the island. On the west side of the bridge is the Caribbean sea which is a light turquoise blue in stark contrast to that not more than a fifty feet over is the raging deep navy blue tongue of the Atlantic Ocean. This site was very memorable for Angela. We took photos there and exchanged smiles as we dreamed of the beauty of the day and thought on the beauty of the evening soon to come. The beauty observed here at the glass windows bridge is memorable, its active beauty with the wave action of the two contrasting sides meeting below as they crash together producing waves and streams of white foam wet and dripping from the rocks surface like the essence of a life force maintained by the contrasting seas. The bright morning sun shone down as we enjoyed the beauty of the morning and after this I realized that Angela was becoming accustomed to the heat of the day. All that she was taking in had seduced her and taken away her fear of the hot summer sun. After strolling this romantic isle of stone we jumped into the jeep once again and headed on our way to the enchanting island of, Harbor Island.

The dock at Three Islands, the harbor on Eleuthera adjourning Harbor Island, was crowded that morning; there was much activity. The water taxis buzzed in and out with passengers. The taxi drivers actively solicited invitations for guests to cruise with them and the breeze of the bay at Three Island dock mesmerized us. I had already given up my memory of Tarpum Bay and was looking forward to the fun and pleasure filled day we would experienced on the small island which held such charm and excitement in its name. The choppy dialect of the island taxis buzzed around us as one of the gentleman held his hand fixed for Angela to step aboard while he loaded the boat for the short trip across to," Briland." White foam, water, choppy water all around as the boat hastily and powerfully pulled out from the dock making its way through the ocean spray toward the near island. Already on the wind the excitement drifted toward us. My mind further shifted as I thought briefly about the conch salad stand and the pure process with which the soft white flesh is prepared. I felt the excitement of the moment; by the look on her face my guest did too. She was smiling and busy placing her hair in the wind as the package delivery girl from UPS rapped with the driver and snickered in their familiar coded grin. I looked over at Angela and became moved with this thing I had done. Here I had met this beautiful stranger and gotten to know and trust her, vice versa, and now together we were about to experience one of the most wonderful and free days of my life. I was living now and I knew it. I felt it in the water splashing, I felt my mind jiggly with relaxation, and gently I caressed Angela's hand to remind her of how special she was to me, to remind her of the moment. We were there where we wanted to be, increasing and going into the moment we both longed for. We were at last free of distance, free of communications, we were happy with the crew among the white caps. I cherish that moment. After the brief crossing we arrived at Harbor Island dock, helped of by the drivers we walked along the walk way toward the town hungrily taking in the simple bright beauty of," Tuesday on the run"- of getting away from it all. Earlier we had discussed on the phone our opinions on race and her likeness of the beautiful black man. Now here we were away from all this mess and move together like a metaphor to enjoy the scenic beautiful of this minute island paradise. Just around the corner was Valentines yacht club, not so far away from that was everything, in walking distance. All this fun and beauty in one little place is fantastic. I longed for Eleuthera to taste it. I love to caress and thus I did gently rubbing and holding habitually out of a tender love to please. Angela was getting used to this.

Ahead of us directly to the right was the Bay Street of Harbor Island. Its buzzling and busy all day with golf carts and traffic on foot, tourists and locals alike up and down trying that day to find something to please. I had mine and needed some entertainment and good times between us. We rented a golf cart at the dock and with the operation instructions pressed off up the dock toward Bay Street to find some pleasure. We were hungry after the long drive and headed to an elegant pink restaurant, which by the looks promised to serve us a great meal and leave us with lots of energy for the remainder of the day. Slowly we dined on burgers, conch chowder and fritters until the palette was filled, leaving enough room for the delicious conch salad that was soon to follow. We then proceeded toward the conch shack up yonder toward the power station passing the many brilliantly colored wooden houses which have survived generations of mischief in this little town and stood strong as monuments of the temperament of these wonderful people. Some of these beautiful houses painted in all white with pastel color trimming, others bright red trim or blue, all so lovely standing as a testament of care and time. Soon we arrived at the conch stall where the lady was preparing some of the most delicious dished in Bahamian cuisine. The roar conch freshly made into a salad is the most delicious dish I have ever had. Seasoned correctly with citrus juices, salt and peppers it's so delicious. These folks make hundreds of conch salads daily here at this stall so there is no wondering why it's the best place for conch salad in the world. The gentleman in the water at the back chops and removes the conch, then cleans it leaving only the crunchy moist white flesh exposed and ready to be sliced into small cubes for the conch salad which is a blend of onions, sweet pepper, black pepper, citrus juices including lime and orange, many tiny squares of conch and an appropriate dash of salt. Its really the most wonderful fresh dish you can find anywhere in the world. Angela had fun since this was her first time eating the salad. She told me that she wanted to try conch in all the ways we made it and again today she was getting that chance. It's delightful. She watched as I did the man chop the conch out of the shell, skin it and pack it for the table. We both took photographs of the process and waited with wet mouths for the completion of the fresh salads. The lady did a great job and pushed them gently toward us for our liking. We had a great time savoring the first limy citrus bite as our taste buds were overcome with excitement. This was Truly a citrus zest of excitement for the taste buds. Angela loved it.

After our sumptuous lunch we headed for the straw market at the foot of the docks where Angela saw some baskets or bags that she liked and thought they would be helpful for her during her trip to carry around items. She bargained with the lady and bought two beautiful rope bags, a large one for towels and such, a small one for the wallets and jewelry while at the beach these will come in handy and they truly did the entire trip. Our next excursion was the beautiful Pink Sands Hotel where we sipped fruity tropical drinks and over looked the wonderful Atlantic pink sandy beach. Its truly wonderful and I think it one of the best-kept, cleanest beaches in the world. If all our beaches met this standard we'd have no problem whatsoever. After sipping these fruity delights at the bar we scurried down to the beach area to sit in the sand and view life as the rich and famous sees it. We'd relax for a while the remainder of the afternoon and enjoy the surf and sand, allowing Angela a chance to work on her tan. She was doing good, getting red at least and wanted to advance to brown as soon as she could. I on the other hand had no problem. I'm always a light brown handsome man with lots of chocolate to share, I was delighted however to explore the ridges of Angela's back however as I applied, as I was commissioned to do, the sun tan oil to every crevice and smooth surface I could find. Angela was a beautiful girl. She glistened in the sun, turning red wherever exposed to the sun. Her face was already tan after this the second day so surely she would get the tan of her life in the two weeks we had planned. She would go home to California with something to show of her vacation in the Bahamas, along with lots of great pleasant memories on her mind. I would see to that. It had been eight years I told her since I was last this close to a woman so I was grateful to have her near. She had seen a man one year ago and had had no one since so I felt happy being the next man in this single mothers life. Her charm, beauty and great spirits made me proud that she had taken this chance to be with me. These great circumstances that allowed us to be together were coming together today.

I would have to visit my friends at Run away Hill. It was at Run away Hill that I first experienced life. I consider these women very special and think about them and the precious moments we shared quite often. I assured Angela that I was more of a flirt than a run around. I had explained to her earlier on the phone that there was not an opportunity for me to meet many women on the island. The point is that once we here on the island reach the age of eighteen we have to leave the island to seek work else where, most likely Nassau or some other city of the world. As a result of this most of the eligible intelligent women on the island had left to go to live in the cities. This fact, I explained to her, is what made me so lonely. There was no one here for me, they were all elsewhere and I was left to find the best way I knew of meeting someone. My experimenting with the Internet was perfect for that reason. I had found her that way and had a real need to meet and see someone. This fact legitimized the whole affair between Angela and I in my mind. I did in fact have a real need for someone. I had a nee for a fine respectable, loving human being to woo, to hold and to love. This our special day at Harbor Island was doing it for me. The lady from Nassau whom I spent some time with at Run Away hill for the firs time was special then too. She was the first. We were two young people deeply in love with each other although my perspective was different now than then. It's much broader and appreciative of love. Its now more tender and understanding of the moment. Not wanting to interfere but wanting to just wait out the moment. I wanted now to find the good stuff, I saw the fantasy in the moment and wanted to make natural and good for Angela, unpretentious and lovely like something out of a novel that one should read about. Patricia had loved me for who I was. My best friend whose parents owned Run away Hill had introduced me to Patricia. He felt then that she was perfect for me and he was right. We are a good match for each other. Both of us needed and were in need of love. We gave to each other the things we needed gently and without thinking of doing otherwise. Our love was splendid, soft and fun. We danced, and treated each other, as young lovers should at every occasion. We had great fantasy and fulfilled each other's dreams beginning, Run away Hill brought back memories. My best friend had given me this best gift and I wanted to see his people, as I hadn't in those past eight years. His mother was the head cook as well at the resort and my memories of her beautiful smile and hospitality to me eight years ago were quite grand. Patricia and I had come over from Nassau as part of a foursome couple with my best friend and his girl and were given a special room close to the beach by him for the reason he knew only too well. He wanted me to have the best time in Briland that I ever had in my life. I did. Patricia made me very happy at about midnight after we retired from the main dining room and an evening of enchanting fun with our friends. Now I was reliving this wonder experience with Angela and was having more fun and giving up more to the total experienced. That is where the enjoyment came in. Anything could happen between Angela and I that day and I didn't care, I was in love with this woman and I tried every moment to show her my love and affection. I longed for nothing now she was with me. I only needed to show her how I felt and evoke her honesty and awaken her loving feelings and the rest would be magic. I longed for us both to float of that magic carpet of love forgetting every moment but just going on and on and on in that light airy malaise that surrounds lovers. This is what went on underneath the movements that were becoming after today more and more synchronized more magical, more surrender.

We sat gently on the most amazing beach I had ever seen and watched the ocean as I glanced over at Angela and occasionally reached over and caressed her. Already we were the best of friends and any moment now the magic could happen for the first time between us. Our stay on the Pink Sands Beach of Harbor Island lasted about two hours. After occasional dips in the cool, clear waters then laying out on the sunning chairs we were ready for the next adventure which was the trek down the island to Runaway Hill to meet again my friends parents. We walked back up the sandy hill to the golf cart and started out down the island road to Run away Hill. Mrs. Thompson was quite happy to see me again. I don't know how much she knew of what was going on at the earlier visit to Run away hill with Patricia but she seemed to be quite understanding and helpful at all times. Always wearing that broad charming smile she has become known for. She offered us lunch but we refused having just sampled so much earlier of the island cuisine. We soon exchanged best wishes after her meeting Angela and we headed off again to kill the remainder of our time till 4 o'clock when we planned to head back to the main land and back to Hiltons Haven in Tarpum Bay. We worked more then on the golf cart tour of the island using the crude map given at the dock we navigated practically the whole island in about an hour. It's so populated, small and nice. Off we went shortly after 4pm back to the mainland by water taxi. Back to reality with sugar plums dancing in our heads and a mirthy feeling of mutual friendship and a very excellent memory we would have with us for the remainder of our lives. The sun was still warm and the Three-island dock still buzzing with activity at that time of the day. My green jeep was park in its usual place and we felt quite good about having had a fun day and heading back home for what was to come next. Later that evening after resting we had succulent Barbecue ribs, lettuce salad and Macaroni from Barbies restaurant in Tarpum Bay. Barbie had prepared, at our request, a take out order. We were somewhat exhausted from the trip and Angela wanted to get another long night of rest so I left her early to return to her the following morning for another fun day of exploring.

Chapter three

Wednesday the 07th of August
Touring the Deep South

I awoke very excited the next morning with imaginations of where we would tour this nice day in Eleuthera. Lately the weather had been great. We had gone three months without a drop of rain. Although the farmers were worried I was feeling great and hoping the rain stayed up in the sky for at least another two weeks. I didn't feel the shortage of water right now and needed nothing negative to affect my plans at the moment. In addition to that I was very interested at this time to making closer moves toward Angela. She had been here for two days now and I longed for a more affectionate taste of romance that I had come to expect from her over the telephone. So far we had been touching each other, holding hands and giving each other brief kisses that made my body tingle with excitement. I felt now the need to go deeper. She was here because I loved and needed her and I wanted to explore the greater possibility of our falling in love with one another and doing something great together for us, like falling into a long-term long distance relationship. I was open to the possibility of marriage if she were willing and if things worked out in that direction. I was lonely at that time and emotionally she had made my dream come true of having someone there for me when I needed to make someone smile and I wanted to fulfill this dream to the fullest. I am not accustomed to being an empty dreamer. I dream and produce my reality out of the substance of my dreams and now today was another day my dream of totally having her was coming true.

I awoke took my shower, cleaned up and left the house smelling nice in the best cologne I had at around 9am. Angela had slept in that morning. Perhaps a little tired from the previous day and in need of a few hours extra indulgence seeing that it was her vacation time.

Shortly after we got dressed again and made plans for the day. It was now 10am and we took off in the jeep again. This time headed south, as far south as we could go. I planned this day to show Angela a beach, which I myself had not seen in some 14 years. In fact I had only been there once in my life but the popularity of this beach is so great I knew I had to go. I wanted to see everything here again with Angela. I wanted to expose to her all of what I had to offer and all I could give her if she decided to stay with me here in the Bahamas. I was prepared for that although I knew it would be tough I wanted this gorgeous blonde for myself and held nothing back in attempting to get her and keep her within my clutches.

We had to pack a lunch for this occasion since there are no restaurants in these southern areas, although Sheryl's is a long drive away to the west. I felt it was too far away and decided to pack some of Nellie's famous burgers for us along with some nice cold cokes and of course some of her delicious apple turnovers. We stopped by Nellie's bakery and ordered while we waited for the order our eyes sampled the many hand made cakes and candies Ms. Nelly had to offer. She is one of the best bakers on the island and one can count of finding her available any day except Sunday to serve among the best meals you can find on the island. Her burgers were a good bet. They are by far the best I have tasted any where in my many travels. We had gotten something to have for breakfast along the way. Just a slight snack of juice and crackers from the supermarket on the highway up the way to Rock Sound. My budget was not as hefty as I would have liked for it to be but I knew if we took the frugal approach to the situation we would have enough money to last throughout the trip and on into the trip to Nassau as well. I could go to the bank for more money but I didn't want to do too much of this since I still have business expenses to consider after Angela heads back to the States, if she allows that to happen. I would do the best that I can and afford her the best vacation that I could under the circumstances anyway and today I was feeling just like that, spend, spend, and spend. Angela knew she had made me happy with the events of the morning. We were both happier. I would have to find some means of changing her view and making her realize that she is here to please me although I would not in any circumstances demand that she do so. I wanted her to come to understand as she did before that she is here with me because I am a man who is lonely and needs love. Love given passionately and freely, I would not demand anything other than that from her. Somehow through osmosis or the understanding of my need through my environment she would have to come to understand that. She would have to know that this was the purpose of my entire constant feeling and caressing. This is the message I was sending to her that she needed to understand on her own. I needed her to know I would settle for no less than love and understanding.

After our visit to the bakery we stopped at the travel agency in order to reschedule the tickets for Angela to leave for the US out of Nassau rather than from Governors Harbor as the tickets were initially scheduled to do. I decided to show her Nassau and knew that our living together in the same room in a hotel in Nassau would bring us even closer together. This time of living alone in Eleuthera would show Angela that I respected her and understood her need for some down time, some time to get lonely and think further of how we would be together I would have to work by the plan and hope that things would work out the way that I thought they would. So far the plans were doing great. The travel agent informed us that the tickets could be changed but with a penalty by Delta airlines or by the American Eagle. Either airline could do the arrangements and since we did not have the tickets with us she suggested that we wait until we were in Nassau to make the changes. I felt relieved that they could be changed. I did want for Angela to see Nassau. I simply wanted her to be able to see the contrast between the island, Eleuthera, where I live and the cityscape of Nassau, which is so different in comparison. Angela was from cattle country in California so she understood and appreciated the sparseness of population on my island. She could see the vast area of uninhabited vegetation that is the island. There is predominately here, natural beauty that cannot be denied and there is also unspoken protectionist legislation in the land for this pristine non-developed beauty to be preserved for the sake of our country and for the appreciation of those generations who will come behind us. Angela could see this and she did express her amazement to me that every beach that we are on we had the whole beach to ourselves with the exception of Harbor Island. There are simply very few people here. Those that are here have many more concerns in their daily lives than the beaches. They are busy trying to make a living and making the ends meet for putting food on the table for the family. Not many of us take vacations and stay at home infact to enjoy our own beaches. It is simply not done. Mostly our visitors who keep coming back year-to-year enjoy our beaches. We do love that.

After our visit to the travel agency we took off again with the intention that our next stop be Light House beach. We passed through the remainder of Rock Sound, and then on into the resort area of Cotton Bay, next we passed through the sleepy town of Whymm's Bight and on to Bannerman Town. The drive was a long and exhausting one. It was hot and on most of these days we were consuming, from our cooler, lots of very cold Eleuthera Pure water.

The road to Bannerman town is so rough. It is totally unkempt and narrow. I did not remember the exact road to travel but since we were on this very rough one so far I decided to see it to its end and I did. Along the way we met a small truck of locals searching for crab in the famous crab land of Bannerman town. Crabs crawl there since it is not inhabited and because of the rough terrain in which the like to live. Since crab and rich is a delicacy in the Bahamas and a favorite meal these guys are busy searching for them mostly after it rains but it hadn't and they were still there. They assured us that we were on the correct road to lighthouse beach and informed us of their wishes for soda pop. Since we had none we reluctantly moved on down the narrow path in hopes of soon seeing the beautiful beach everyone talks so much about. After many bumps and scrapes we eventually did. From a distance we saw the lighthouse on top of the distant hills and made off toward the hills knowing the beach would be there. Just before getting there we witnessed a seldom seen sight in this area of the world, an eagle had made a nest atop a giant dead cedar out of the reach of any predator, its was an amazing and lovely sight of which we got a few photographs. We moved on toward the Light House beach.

Once there and off the winding sandy road we saw the spectacular beach. Just seeing a great scene is enticing enough. Knowing that you have it all to yourself for as long as you wished is another thing. We saw absolutely no one in sight. The beach was much like the beach at Harbor Island, that beautiful only it had more reefs and beautiful waters known for its diving and snorkeling. Some of the most exciting snorkeling and fishing can be had on this uninhabited beach. We were there to enjoy as much of it as we wished. Angela laid out the towels from her new rope bag and we lay there on the deserted sand like two people who owned a world. We were like two people who were having some fun and wanted it to wait for us until we were ready. This was the time to totally relax and enjoy the surf. I remembered they say that you can see Cat Island from this beach on a clear day and sure enough I did see a land mass. They call that one Little Sansalvador but you can see Cat Island from the hill and the lighthouse on a good clear day. I explored all of this. Soon after we took a walk down the beach Angela looking for shells and other treasures she might find in the sand. I went on with my camera to get a glimpse of the Light House. I wanted some pictures for my collection. On this trip as well I was photographing the island, all the beaches and places we visited I would add to my collection. I wanted them the photographs, I wanted to have them. I needed some memento of this great time, of this great island, which I was rediscovering through Angela. The Lighthouse was fantastic. I saw that someone had installed a new modern light with solar panels and no doubt a photocell at some expense in order to keep the lighthouse going. So it is an active light house not just some touristic relic. I don't know how old it is but I know that it has been around for a few generations and dates back to the pirate days when they hid treasure along the shorelines of this very island. In fact a few years earlier some gold had been found there. It was now a part of our national treasure. The gold and artifact were along with other artifacts kept in good stead by our government archival department. The fresh water well at the lighthouse fill to the rim with green water was covered in graffiti and other forms of engraving. It stood as a testament to the many visitors who had frequented the lighthouse over the years. The small kitchen house with its Dutch oven was still an active structure and there were signs of fairly recent usage as ashes and coal lay in the furnace cold but evidence of some cooks making. The open structure of the light house was intact, the wooden floor and the roof in remarkable shape, I observed as I soaked up the history and thought of the many mysterious happenings and goings on in this isolated otherwise lonely place we had come to visit. This area is quite remote from civilization and is several times reported to be the place of rumored mischief so I soon got back to Angela to absorb some more of its beauty and woo my love into wanting me more. We laid ourselves some more on the warm white sand, although white, pristine with the occasional glitter of pink; it's not as pink as that of Harbor Island. A little more we dipped our warm bodies in the Atlantic Ocean. The Atlantic Ocean protected by the many reefs between us and the surf reaching as far and beyond the horizon as one can see. It was, every moment of it, magnificent. I had no memory of another life now. I was in the moment and totally devoted to enjoying the pleasure of this reality. I felt at this time that as far as beaches were concerned Lighthouse beach and Pink Sands beach at Harbor Island were the two best beaches I had ever seen in my life and I have seen a lot of beaches. They are wider with a direct view of the Atlantic ocean that feeds them and they are clean, light house beach by the natural action of the ocean since no one is ever around there.

For several hours we enjoyed our time together at Lighthouse beach. We bathed in the rich turquoise waters, sunned on the pristine white beach and had our lunch in between, the Nelly burgers. It was all so nice. I had never experienced a day quite like this one. This one was special. I knew that I would remember this day and long again for a day like this for a long time to come. It was mine and no one else's now and I took it in hand as I did the two previous days. I was having the time of my life with this beautiful woman who I could now say was my own. We were as together now as we could be. We had come to love one another intensely in this short period of time and tried tenderly to fulfill the fantasy of the other. I was getting deeper and deeper into loving Angela's curvaceous body and alluring tight ass. I would for the time she was with me give her a love that would be easy to remember. I would be hard to forget.

After a full afternoon of such enjoyment and with some reluctance we moved on. We were far up the island and wanted to be on our way before it got too late in this isolated paradise. I would let no harm come to my darling and my every move proved it. I planned cautiously and moved about with a sense of care taking and caution. With as much care that we took entering the narrow bush filled road leading to Light house beach we exited with as much. The journey out of the beach road was briefer than it had been entering it. It seemed shorter. On our way out we stopped and checked close up the nest of the hawk that rested nearby in the tall dead cedar tree. It seemed splendid and filled me with a sense of adventure. I felt like I was a natural observer of wildlife in action. There above in the tree was the unusual sight of the hawk and the huge nest he had made in this isolated place even south of Bannerman town. So isolated there was nobody here for long periods of time at all. Only those who have experienced the beauty of the place returned on pilgrimages to this great beauty and adventure, this isolation.

For what seemed like a few minutes we drove through Bannerman town and ended up at the tip of that side of the island again. We came upon Princess Cay. This also isolated beach compound is owned by the cruise line industry, which uses it as a rest stop or destination for their passengers passing as most of them do along this tip of the island. This Cay is not a Cay but is market as such so as not to alert the passengers that they are actually on a large populated island. For some reason they have chosen to keep it a secret from their cruise passengers. For some reason the tourists are not allowed and encouraged to tours our lovely island. For the moment I don't know the answer to this mystery and can't understand their motivation for doing this. I wish to share this island paradise we have here with as many people as wish to share it. There is much beauty here and there is certain resentment among the natives that the ships do not allow their passengers to tour the island. Princess Cay is wonderful. They have a lovely beach area with every type of water sports imaginable and several wonderful bars and dining areas to accommodate as many guests that come aboard to enjoy the daylong stop over.

There were several places I wanted Angela to see in this southern most part of the island. After a slow relaxing drive through Whymm's Bight we took a brief tour of Davis Harbor and viewed the many yacht and harbored fishing vessels residing there. There is not much to see at Davis Harbor other than the harbor itself but along with this tour it was fine and provided somewhere else for us to see and enjoy during this pleasant day. Next we drove on into the settlement of Deep Creek and on into the resort area of Cape Eleuthera. Cape Eleuthera used to be a grand Golf resort community. All of the Golf greats toured the course in its heyday and enjoyed the best that a vacation had to offer in this lovely resort area.

Unfortunately the resort is no longer functioning and the harbor is the only attraction there these days. Its a lovely deep water harbor the likes of which you cannot find anywhere in this part of the world. It is a grand sight to see and is famous for other reasons. The Atlantic Ocean has an area called the tongue of the Ocean just one mile off the coast of this harbor. This drop in the Ocean floor called the tongue of the ocean is famous as a test sight for US nuclear submarines. It is a testing ground for Nuclear sub maneuvers the likes of which can be seen towering above the horizon when these maneuvers are going on. The US soldiers for these maneuvers are flown into the airport at Rock Sound, Eleuthera and taken by taxi to the harbor at Cape Eleuthera. Once there they are transported by boat out into the horizon to live for the next short while aboard a waiting nuclear submarine. Just the size of the submarine towering above the horizon is intimidating, not to mention its capability. There would be no subs here today but Angela needed to see this area. I wanted her to plant all these areas in her mind and remember and treasure them as much as I did. I wanted to marry Angela and have here moved here to the Bahamas to live with me. I needed her. I needed someone to love me, to live with me and be my companion. I was lonely here for many reasons and Angela filled the void that I had inside. If everyday we shared together would be as special as this one, I knew I needed it. I needed the chance not to be lonely and certainly with Angela by my side I would be happy. We would be happy together. I had worked hard over the years and had so much going for me. My business was lucrative. I was making lots of money. I had just completed my

latest project, a commercial building which was now
housing a tenant who ran in the space a clothes store. I
was doing fine financially and now wanted to complete
my dreams by marrying Angela and moving her in
with me. I had not asked her to marry me as yet but
hoped deep inside that she too shared this dream of
loving and living together with me.

Cape Eleuthera was still fine and made a great
memory for us both. There were still guests living in
the town houses there and the harbor master resided
there so it was not too lonely a place to visit although it
was no where near the splendor it shared during it
grand heydays back in the late seventies. The afternoon
was wearing on, it was now about 4:30 PM and there
would be one last stop along the tour for Angela this
afternoon. I could not let her go without seeing the
splendid beauty of Cotton Bay Golf Resort. This
Resort was built by very rich captains of American
industry during the late sixties and was now a world
famous resort and golf area, although the hotel is
closed at this moment. Many of these rich, elite
persons still own family homes on the, "Ridge of
Cotton Bay," as it is called. Although its place is
somewhat diminished from the travel market these
days the beauty of this area is alive, it cannot be
mistaken or missed. The main golf course and resort sit
above on of the loveliest beach areas in the world. The
pristine white sands of the beach bend around corners
and travel along the Atlantic coast for miles. This is
one of the most enjoyable areas and one of the most
celebrated we have ever had developed. The
contribution of Cotton Bays original owners to this
island of ours is enormous. They collectively are

responsible with the civilization of the South Eleuthera area during the years they resided with us here. This area known as, "South Eleuthera," is near and dear to many of their hearts and many of them made it a life's work to see that the area was developed to the point it is today. People like, Arthur Vining Davis, Juan Tripp of Pan American Airlines, The Ames family of Illinois and several others made this area of Cotton Bay one to be remembered. It still lives on today. Just in front of the gigantic empty resort the 18 hole golf course stretches for several miles. Its beauty and uniqueness to the island unchallenged. Angela had to see Cotton Bay, I was glad to be with her. After what seemed like an hour of touring the beach, the golf course, all of the wonderfully painted homes with immaculate lawns we were ready to go home to Tarpum Bay for the evening. We had spent a wonderful sunny day together and had explored so much more than the landscape. We knew each other. I knew when to touch Angela, or tickle her, touch her breast and make her smile. She was new, exciting and freest to me. I wanted more.

The drive home took about twenty minutes. I left Angela at the motel to shower, get rest and returned later that evening with a Pizza from Barbies restaurant in the heart of Tarpum Bay. We passed the evening away on the front porch of the motel room chatting, nibbling and my feeling my way for the next opportunity to feel the sweet juices in Angela's pants. I left Angela alone that night at around 10 PM. I wanted her to have some space and rest for the adventure of the coming day.

Chapter four

Thursday 09th of August
New in love

It was Thursday and the week was wearing on. I juggled my plan around in my mind and hoped that the remainder of the week until Tuesday was sufficient for us to see all that there was to see on Eleuthera. There was so much to see, so much to do. I decided to take each day at a time and do as much as we could together as long as we were together, that is what mattered most.

Today would be another adventure. I had all the time in the world to do with Angela as I wished and all of this beautiful territory to do it in. I had planned a trip to the center of the island. I wanted to tour and see all that this area had to offer. There were a few things, Cupids Cay, the earliest original settlement of the country. There were also the towering hills overlooking Cupids Cay from the other side of the island. The Banks road on the Atlantic side of the island ran along one of the longest most memorable beaches on the island and was the most populated area of foreigner owned homes. That usually means lots of money. These houses are spectacular and I wanted Angela to see them. I had dreams of living in this style; in this type of neighborhood one day so formulating plans with her by my side was in the right perspective for me. Angela was already awakening and by the time I got to the motel. Unlike me she was an early riser and arose with the sun early and excited wanting to take more of our fair island paradise. As usual we had breakfast along the way. Usually some chips and a punch or soda. That was faster than waiting around for eggs and bacon. I was not a real breakfast person, neither was Angela. She told me earlier how she was accustomed to eating one meal per day. I wondered to myself how she got by. I needed so much more than that to keep me going and am quite fond of two to three meals most days.

I prayed again this morning for clear sunny skies. It had not rained for three months here and it was still relatively dry. There was only one incidence of rain the very first day that Angela arrived. It rained briefly on the way from the airport then later that day while at the beach at North Side. Angela loves the rain. She remarked at how warm it was. She just walked along as I did, knowing it was just a passing shower, holding out her hand catching the cool rain drops amazed at their temperature compared to the rain in California. I didn't want any more rain to interrupt what we had going. It remained sunny now each day with little chance of showers in sight, for that I was glad and reminded myself of how much the farmers needed rain. That thought made me thankful for whatever came my way and I was glad to accept this and was learning to enjoy whatever did. The drive up to Governors was pleasant and quiet. Angela just sat back and enjoyed the scenery while I drove on enjoying each moment myself, occasionally stopping for that perfect photograph which I planned to publish somewhere to display first hand the beauty of this island home of mine. It was like I was on a campaign lately. I had talked on the radio and on the Internet with so many people, all of which were in awe of the beauty of the

Bahamas. I was now on a crusade to win the world over to coming in to enjoy the splendors of nature I had enjoyed for my whole life give or take the few years I was away in college. I had come back from all that because I had seen the world and did remember the beauty we had here. I had felt the isolation and loneliness of city living and at that time longed for the friendliness and good living I remembered while growing up as a young boy. Over the past six years I had rediscovered that beauty of living in people and in nature and was now on a crusade to share that with those I came into contact with. This was my mission and this was my first hand opportunity to see it work. I got no complaints from Angela. She spoke of no ecological disaster or imbalance of nature. She sat beside me an arms length away thinking as I did of the splendid ness of this island paradise we all had. Since it was so much in our nature to share, I wanted to first hand and I did. I had worked quite hard at my business over the last three months collecting and depositing as I was so good at doing, providing a way to make all this happen. The plans were quite sketchy in mind as to how it would all take place but it was taking shape now. I didn't know how to exactly plan for it but it did happen. I had sent the plane tickets and kept in touch daily with Angela by the PC and by the telephone. I had won her confidence over and assured her of safety and other matters of concern. She was here because I loved her. I was lonely and needed someone to hold and to hold me, that's why she was here and she knew. I treated her that way. I showed her that I appreciated every moment she was with me. I loved her. That she would be mine was my next wish, these several days would prove what was to be.

So on we drove up to Governors Harbor. The drive from Tarpum Bay is quite a scenic one. Between Tarpum Bay and Savannah Sound all you see along the way is the turquoise beauty of the water. The centuries old black rock separating the road and the water is just lying there strong and rippled with character. The tall green cedars broken occasionally with the green lush of other vegetation making a fantastic collage of a slide show as one drives along the seashore road up the island to Governors Harbor. Between Savannah Sound and Palmetto Point there is the fresh green lush of vegetation capping the rolling hills, which stretch in all directions as far as the eyes, can see. This is the undeveloped landscape of future promise. One of these days in some generation this beauty will not be observed. For some of us this is a saddening thought. The turtle ponds from which my uncle fished for turtle are still in existence on the outskirts of Palmetto Point along the highway as we drove steadily and free up the highway to the rising hills of Governors Harbor. The red clay soil so famously known for its growth of Pineapples exposed by the company tractors clearing the high-tension lines along the winding highway. This is a beautiful way to spend the morning. Added to this beauty are the numerous bright red Poinciana's just recently showing their annual splendid display of color. The redness of these flowers spaced randomly among the greenery of the lush wilderness among the rolling hills is satisfying. Nature has shown its face again and I have promised to photograph as many of these trees as I can in order to capture this natural beauty. I had done some of that. During each days outing I would take the camera and capture all of the picturesque worthy sights I saw along the way. I had a digital camera where I would download the photos onto the computer so they were available for viewing instantaneously. I now had a wonderful collection of photos for Angela and I to view whenever we got the chance. I promised to email most of these photos to her so that she could show her friends back home where she had been on holiday. She was in love with the whole plan; I loved her for that. She was easygoing and charming, not to mention understanding of my loneliness now that she saw the vast undeveloped landscape that I was from. I explained to her how all of our population had to make a choice to leave this island or stay when they were of age. Our tragedy is that we don't have any jobs here. There is not much industry and not very much infrastructure. Our government is just now building on that. I explained to her that we have a long way to go and that this was my effort, my life, to assist our people and help our economy develop. I didn't know how much of that I could take in the future but for now I had paradise right with me so I was not worried. Paradise I explained to her is like a paradox. You can have one or the other. You have the natural beauty of the landscape or you have the developed beauty of man. I enjoyed nature and the beginnings that I had. I had chosen the everlasting beauty of nature, much the same as I had chosen Angela. Her natural beauty and caring personality captured me. All else was secondary. She was nature.

We headed into Governors harbor with fervor and anticipation. We hoped to find things here in our days travel that would last in our memory forever. Those things were here it was up to us to find them. Cupids Cay was as lovely as ever. The Methodist church stood out clearly from the back road to the Cay, past the old restored Hayne's Library at the foot of the bridge leading out to the small Cay. The colorful residences were aglow in the bright morning sun, standing in contrast to the beautiful calm waters sparkling and dipping with the boats that lined the harbor. The water shone like crystal in some areas the small choppy wave shone back at us letting us know that they too were part of the picture that makes this harbor so memorable. Across from the Cay in the far left corner of the hidden cove were the bright rainbow colors of the sails on the sunfish boats owned by Club Med which had its home on the Atlantic shore but used the harbor for its water sports facility. The waters were teeming with small craft and Jet Ski's. The happy screams of vacationing tourist enjoying the water were heard in the distance along with the slow moving traffic frequenting the Cay. In addition to that the chirping of the birds and the crowing of roosters on the roost were heard in the background. This was a pleasant place to be on a Thursday morning. The workers at customs in front of the big bright pink warehouse loafed for the moment and sat waiting for the next freight ship to land at their shores with goods from Florida. They would then get into action. Further in the back of the island the dilapidated state of some of the housing was evident. Ronnie's Bar and dance hall now dominated the landscape with it bright blue and rainbow colors. This location was painted in a fashion so as to warn visitors to the excitement and fun that goes on here from sun down to the wee wee hours of the morning. My brother is heard to say many days," Boy Ronnie's was hopping last night." But now it was day and the sun was hot. There was no time for stopping. The air-conditioning in the jeep was on high and made the morning drive that much more enjoyable. Angela had drove past the Cay and through Governors now several times once from the airport then again on the way to Harbor Island but now she was seeing it up close. I explained to her that this was the birthplace of this entire nation. I told her of how the Pilgrims journeyed from Bermuda to Cupids Cay to colonize it during the late 1700's. They were seeking religious freedom from persecution in Bermuda and they found the perfect place for their habitation. After viewing Cupids Cay we had lunch at the Blue Room where we savored fresh fried fish and dined on crab and rice with cold Pepsi and a side dish of cole slaw.

Lunch was magnificent and so was the view from the high hills overlooking Cupids Cay in the more developed part of Governors Harbor. The hills are so high. One can hardly walk up and down these hills and must take extreme caution driving up and down. This is the highest point on the island and is the location for the islands telecommunication antennas and company. Their tower can be seen for miles at sea at night and for miles around during the day. The bright white and red mast juts high into the air and contains the antennas necessary for inter island communications. This is also a most memorable sight and is painted most frequently by most artist who frequent and live on the island. My neighbor, the artist Mal Flanders has many scenes depicting both Cupids Cay and the settlement of Governors Harbor and its unique sites. We journeyed on from the peak of the hills down the backside of the hills and onto the Banks road, which is the Atlantic side of the island and at the beginning of which is the Club Med resort, we are so famously known for. This area known as the Banks road is one of the original tourist areas on the island because of its beautiful Atlantic beaches, which stretch for numerous miles. This beach is perhaps the longest and most beautiful white sandy beach on the Atlantic side of the island and attracts some of the most famous world travelers who visit our shores. The entire length of the road, some eight miles, is filled on both sides with exotic homes of rich Americans and Europeans alike. The road winds and bends around several corners and comes to an end on the backstretch of Palmetto point. Where it continues on the other side and contains such nice tourist dwellings and local businesses like the famous, "Uniques," restaurant a place where some of the most delicious sumptuous dining on the island is to be had. It is all quite a sight to see and is all quite splendid. All along the road is the lush greenery of well-kept lawns and quite elaborate attempts at beautifying ones drive way and property. You can see from the Banks road that homeowner of some renowned take great pride in maintaining unique and special looking properties. No two-drive ways are alike which makes touring and viewing this area quite unique itself. We stopped at one home on the waterfront that really stood out to us. The home was painted all white with tall clear glass windows from floor to ceiling on the second floor. We took some photos and I thought to myself," One day I'll own a home just like that." We drove further on and stopped at a spot of grape trees, which had a pathway down to the Atlantic side beach. It was simply gorgeous down there. We again took photographs and returned to the jeep for the remainder of our drive. Up to this point we had been on a whirlwind tour of the island. These several days of touring and beaching were so enchanting and magical. I hoped that it would last forever but knew that the week would end before we knew it. We were having so much fun. We then drove back to Tarpum Bay to Hiltons Haven, Angela stopped in to get some rest for the remainder of the afternoon. I went home to check the email and get some rest myself. I would then plan what to do with the remainder of the day. I was making sure that the action and excitement didn't stop. That there was always something to do and somewhere important to go; that was for sure.

After changing and resting I went back to Hiltons Haven to see Angela who was resting on the bed at the moment. I asked if she would like to see a movie that night. The movie was at eight and it was now six so we would drive to Governors Harbor, have dinner for an hour at the swank Buccaneer Club and then see some black produced movie starring the black rap star Luke from Miami and many of his rap friends. Angela then arose to get ready for the evening. I sensed that she had been a little shy toward me. Since I hadn't been around to watch her dress and undress. Here in front of me she was getting rid of that shyness as she disrobed, showing off those fantastic tits and ass of hers. I sat there like a kid in a candy store as she did this. She was experiencing some anxiety and seemed a bit worried about something. I didn't bother to ask but went along with the program not wanting to interfere too privately for now. Since she explained how close she was to her family back home and they were all worried about her. I assumed that that is what it was. I assumed that she was home sick and signs of it were beginning to show. After all this was the first time she had flown on an airplane and the first time she had been this far away from California. She explained to me that once before she had taken a road trip to Washington State with some friends but that was as far away from home that she had been. I was appreciative of the fact that she had taken such a chance to see me. That she had flown this far overcoming her personal fear of flight just to see some handsome guy in the exotic Bahamas that she felt she could love. Some guy that needed her love and attention, who would give as much loving to her as she knew she needed as well. At times I felt like," yea we really have something special going here." At first I tried not to tell her out loud but eventually it just came out.

Dinner at the Buccaneer club was nice. Bahamian fried chicken with vegetables was a great dish for the evening. I was hungry and felt I needed something substantial to do the job of quenching this hunger. We ordered a few exotic drinks from the bar and spent the hour enjoying the meal and the atmosphere of the club midway between the bottom and the crest of the hill. Their Goombay Smash was delicious; they had a first rate full service bar with and excellent and friendly bar tender. I was pleased to see the scenery as well. From my chair while I chewed was a full eyes view of and evening lit Cupids Cay no doubt sleepy heads in some places getting for the evening drawl and getting ready for bed. We enjoyed our meal and headed there after to the movie theater to enjoy the movie produced and starred in by LA's famous gansta rappers. To our surprise we were the only ones in the movie house. Everyone else were caught up in the independence celebrations that were taking place nation wide or enjoying the opening of the home comings two of which were taking place on the island, one in Savannah Sound the other in the Bluff Eleuthera. I knew we would have time for all that too this weekend and felt a sense of contentment that I had someone lovely and exciting to spend all this time and share all of this excitement with.

Chapter five

Friday 10th of August
Independence Day

I awoke Friday morning with dreams of sugarplums in my head. It was the most important day in the country and everyone would turn out at the park here in every town in the country to celebrate in the form of a formal program. The truly grand celebration and annual Police tattoo took place in Nassau the night before. We wished we were there. I told Angela earlier that we would be spending the next week beginning Tuesday in Nassau. We would take the mail boat ride, carrying the jeep with us into Nassau. There I would have the chance to show her the true grandeur of Eleuthera as compared to the crowded overdeveloped city of Nassau. Nassau is not all bad and does have its specialties like non-stop night life and numerous tours and day activities that Eleuthera doesn't have but you can't beat Eleuthera for the peace and tranquility of life it offers. She would see exactly why I chose to live in the small town, Out Island atmosphere of Eleuthera. I would be able to show here this.

For now this morning there would be celebrating at the park at the dock on the waterfront in Tarpum Bay. I got dressed, drove up to Hiltons Haven where I found Angela still sleeping. She was tiring. This touring was taking its toll. I sat on the bed beside her for a while until she got the rest she needed then watched her as she showered and got dressed for the day ahead. We then drove to the park in Tarpum Bay where we watched the ceremonies take place and enjoyed the local flavor of the festivities. The forum was that of a church service along with that of a political rally since the Member of Parliament was there to speak. Afterwards refreshments were served and all the kids and grown ups were made happy by the handing out of special bags filled with candy, fruit and slices of cake. They all lined up before the tables and one by one filed by for their own special bag of goodies while the brass band played to their delight. I didn't think they did this in America and wanted Angela to see the Bahamian festivities. We then broke out into a discussion of our respective American and Bahamian celebrations, which lasted through, to the end of the ceremonies. We were then ready at about 10 am to continue on our tour for the remainder of the day. I had become intrigued as of late with Bluff Eleuthera. I had only been there once in my life before, although I knew several people that lived there including a defense force officer who had drowned during duty several months earlier. He was a dear friend and I thought of him each time I thought of the Bluff Eleuthera. I would take Angela there today hoping to find a good time and enjoy their homecoming with them. We drove north again pleasantly enjoying the scenery going north. We passed through all the same towns as we did these several days before but each time is new. Each time the scenery changes according to ones mood. Coves and shorelines change with the tide. The road cleaning machine cut grass and clean different areas rearranging the scenery along the side of the road giving one something slightly different to view. I was particularly live today touching and playing with Angela's beautiful soft breasts. I loved her wonderful blonde hair and her shining blue eyes, as she looked back at me with playful and happy glances, sometimes hiding the fact that she needed me this much. She was feeling quite playful and drove beside me as she did most days quite pretty and quiet enjoying the scenery no doubt smiling deep inside at having found such a wonderful friend in me. We passed the Governors Harbor airport about midday. The magnificent view of the clear blue looming below us as it stretched to the western horizon after the airport took its place on the landscape this side of the island. James Cistern was the next small sleepy town along the winding highway and lay sleepily along the Caribbean Sea shore. Here one can tell how much the people love the seashore. Along the highway the serve food in small shacks built hastily by hand. They're famous here for their grand tasting barbecue and other native dishes, which can be purchased daily from several different locations along the seashore in the village. We observed and drove on past the big rock, after the cliffs which we had viewed on the way to Harbor Island, through the Rain Bow Bay Resort area and on into Hatchet Bay where the Silos of yester year stand looming above the landscape as if the scenery was something out of a B movie. The road narrows here and slides along winding into Gregory Town. Evidence of its past glory as the world's largest pineapple producer can be seen in the numerous fields fed by the nutrients of the red clay soil so bright and obvious along the winding highway. The newly paved roads along the highway made traveling such a pleasure. Everything was just so nice on a day like today. The only thing I longed for right at this moment was a large bowl of conch salad seasoned and peppered to my preferment so I longed to reach the homecoming celebration in the Bluff where I could have all of this and more should I want it. Angela lay back to rest a part of the way. I think she was having too much fun and excitement.

Since Angela was resting I went into myself to think. I thought about all of the friends I would meet at the homecoming. My thoughts ran on Ronald my friend who had recently drowned in the service of his country. I thought to myself," What a terrible way to die." I would not let the memory of that great friend go. We had gone to boarding school together and were together like many others in this area," brothers." My mind ran on Brenda the nurse with whom I went to boarding school and who practiced medicine and took care of patients here in Bluff for the Government. I was here she was here. We were alive and well on Eleuthera. Enjoying the beauty and simple splendor of island life. Of course as advertised my friends from ZNS, the countries premiere broadcast facility for television and Radio, a facility where I had worked for some years in the past were there. I would see and have a chance to talk with them. The announcer for Radio Bahamas, Pyswell Socha Forbes, was now here locally. Trained and famous in Jamaica since he schooled there and trained on Jamaican radio his craft was a unique blend of Jamaican and Bahamian traditions. I would have a great time, my second time in this life in Bluff Eleuthera and now among many friends of some renown.

I always did the driving since I trust no one, not ever Angela with my new jeep, which came to a slow stop as we approached the sign that signaled our arrival to the turn off for Bluff Eleuthera. I signaled and turned left and began rubbing Angela's precious tummy and arms in order to gently wake her up to the fact that we were here. The drive into Bluff from the main road was several miles but not too long. We drove throughout the narrow streets of the village and looked around attempting to find our way to the waterfront, which we eventually did. We were famished after that long several hour drive from Tarpum Bay so the first thing that entered my mind after entering the home coming park was the sweet waft of barbecue scent that came from the stalls serving food to which I proceeded with Angela in hand immediately. We ordered two dinners complete with barbecue chicken, peas and rice, potato salad, and cole slaw. The lady sent me over to the other side of the stalls area to purchase some sodas to go with our fabulous lunch. I spotted two spaces open on the benches near the center of the grounds and proceeded there with the food after paying the lady for the food. The meals were simply delicious and took all of my attention immediately since I was in that state. I raised my head for an occasional glimpse of the crowd of people and challenged my barbecue chicken with much zest since I was quite hungry at the time. Once filled and finished with dinner Angela and I proceeded to discard the remnants of dinner and take a walk around the grounds at the dock for a more full view of what was going on. A large group of boys, all in short pants were having fun jumping off the dock and swimming around the mail boat parked at the head of the dock, the MV Day Break. The music from the DJ booth blasted the entire homecoming grounds quite loudly as is traditional at such events; the music is always too loud. I saw those friends of mine who were advertised to be there all week on the radio. There was Soca Forbes wearing his headphones and in his usual grinning and laughter mood. This man enjoys radio and would give anything for a good laugh or a good joke to pick up the festivities. Along with Pyswell was Mario Newry a newer and pleasant DJ spokesperson with a different and more mellow flavor than Pyswell but non the less enjoyable. The entire country tuned in to hear them; the entire country loves them all. Angela and I took seats on a bench on the dock where we had a full view of the entire grounds as well as the dock. I motioned to Angela that I would be going over to say hello to my friends the radio personalities and I did. We spoke briefly and passed greetings. I also saw Tony my former fellow Electronic Engineer at the ZNS station in Nassau. We exchanged greetings as well and I walked back to the bench where Angela was waiting for me. We sat a while and talked. We played with each other while I sat looking constantly for a photograph that I might take to make the occasion memorable. The gigantic Hiltons Mansion dominating the dock and park area with its bright pink painted exterior came into focus. The mere size of this mansion in this small community rose suspicions with me and I told Angela of the few drug lords who have similar opulent homes in certain areas of the island. I did not plan to take her on a tour of these. We soon took in all that there was to see at the homecoming. Angela was shopping now and looking at anklets and bracelets. She had lost a cute dolphin anklet that she purchased in Harbor Island as a gift for a friend back home. She couldn't find it anywhere and this had her perturbed. Since she couldn't find anything like the anklet at any of the stalls she decided to wait till later to purchase one like it. I assured her that she would find something like it once we had a chance to shop the downtown straw market in Nassau where you can find most things of a touristy nature you desire.

I thought deeply about the home coming celebration they were having also in Savannah Sound and felt it would be the ideal place to get us some fresh conch salad for an evening snack once we took the long slow drive back there to Savannah Sound. I decided to take Angela to view the Island of Spanish Wells since it was close by to the north of us. We could wait there till the sun went down and take some more photos of the sunset and the Jane's Bay area during that portion of the evening. We took off a few minutes later taking a slight detour from the main road in the Bluff in order to view some other parts of the town and see more of what the Bluff was about as far as its inhabitants and the buildings were concerned. The houses were so small in comparison to the seaside mansion, which dominated the whole town for that matter. It sat high up on a hill near the dock in the Bluff and could be seen for a short distance since the smaller homes blocked the view from that side of its structure. We went on to the intersection, took a left turn and drove along the narrow winding road passing numerous mango and citrus fruit groves and curry dirt roads until we ended up at Jane's Bay. The view from the dock at Jane's Bay of Spanish Wells was spectacular. The view of the island in the even evening sunlight was beautiful. One could see the island, which got its name from the many Spanish armadas in our past history, which landed there interrupting their sea journeys to replenish themselves with the fresh water contained in the many wells then located on the island. Thus the name Spanish Wells was created. All of this information is recorded as a part of our natural Bahamian history and kept by the department of Archives in Nassau Bahamas. The island of Spanish wells lies out in this portion of the Caribbean Sea about one mile from the Jane's Bay dock. During the day a number of busy ferryboats take passengers and small cargo from the mainland onto the island returning and waiting time after time for more passengers and visitors. This is a brisk and long-term business. The water taxi's make quite a bit of money ferrying passengers from one side of the harbor to the other. At ten dollars a head on a busy day lots of money can be made making this an attractive job among the local Caucasian people. They can be seen and heard with their unique broken brand of English chatting and arguing some times among themselves in their waiting area, a shanty constructed on one side of the small Jane's Bay dock. The younger men are gone most of the year smack fishing and find themselves working long hours fishing, netting and diving for the tons of lobster and other fish that has over the decades made this Caucasian community one of the wealthiest communities in the entire Bahamas. Their drive and desire to work hard and conserve their wealth among themselves has set this community apart in this country. Although many inhabitants cannot appreciate the relative isolation of this community from the mostly black mainlanders they can see the products of their decades long fight to stay ahead of the fishing competition and the surrounding communities. I did not discuss this business with Angela. I didn't want her to know that there was some separation among Eleutherian islanders and here it was before her eyes at Jane's Bay but she could not see beyond the stark glistening ocean and the setting sun perched high above us coming down to the horizon as hot as one can ever imagine. For this same reason I did not take her across to Spanish Wells. I wanted to keep that a secret for her to discover if she ever had the chance to. I did not like discussing racial matters among us. We got along and loved each other up to this point and there was no way I was going to allow some petty issue as the attitude of the Spanish Wellians come in to separate us or cause Angela to second guess or act differently toward me than she had been acting up to this moment. It was a dirty little secret I just could not tell. At least not right now. We had about another hour I estimated before the sun set in the western sky and I decided to spend it exploring another area of the island to which I had only heard about and seen from my travels across and back to the island of Spanish wells. This area was across from the island of Spanish Wells on the mainland. It was an area now inhabited by persons from Spanish Wells who were looking I suppose for more space from the small island. A place where they can be closer to both the mainland and the island of Spanish Wells. I didn't quite know how to get there but I set out to find the quarry road that would lead us in a northerly direction to the ultimate tip of the mainland where there was no tar road and who knows what else. It was a part of today's adventure and we set out in the jeep to find out what there was to see in this direction primarily to kill time before coming back to the dock at Jane's Bay to take photographs of the beautiful setting sun as it dipped below the distant water mark leaving behind the wonderful patterns and colors that interact and play with the clouds for the enjoyment of sun worshippers and tourists like me. The curry road north was rocky and not too smooth but the jeep was able to take this kind of terrain and I felt proud to have this capability and ability to rough it when the time became necessary as it did at many of our beach areas on the island. I worried about the many scrapes made to the smooth paint job I had on the vehicle but I determined that doing this for Angela's and my enjoyment was worth it. I would simply in the future pretend the scratches and marks were not there. Maybe I could wash the marks out with some sort of soap or wax and that thought settled the issue. We soon passed through a village of sorts. It was obvious that this was the small Haitian village I heard about several years earlier that was hit directly, along with the whole northern section of the island, by Hurricane Andrew. The hurricane did so much damage to this Haitian community and to much of North Eleuthera. A few lives were lost and there was much structural damage to many homes in this part of the island. Today there was no sign of that damage. The landscape had recovered over the past six years so had the homes and the people who had witnessed that tragedy. They were all doing fine today. The shantytown through which we were passing now was rough. The homes were constructed flimsily out of pieces of plywood and other types of wood and painted in crude colors. Colorful and crude in their own way and telling of the lives of the few Haitian people who lined the streets and stared at the passing jeep no doubt wondering why these two people had frequented their home village so remote on this day. It was obvious they were resting this evening with the exception of one man who chopped bush in the midst of his flock of goats of in the bushes to the side of the road. The village was a small one where people crouched on crates or nothing. A man sat amidst a group of men curiously wearing a beard of clothes pins from one ear to the next looking like a black Lincoln amidst the laughter of his peers as the play a hand of Haitian cards which I learned to play as a boy and remembered the pain of the clothes pins as the were pinned on the face one after the other as punishment for losing the card game. Despite the pain the game and all the surrounding laughter was so much fun. It was all worth it. We quickly passed through the little shantytown the Haitians have built here for themselves and went on further through the obviously hardly ever-navigated path toward the homes along the western shore of the island that we saw were there. After many bumps and stops to check out which way to turn we came upon a small grassy area in the midst of a small coconut grove. Straight ahead we could see that this was the end of the island since a beach was ahead in the walking distance. I parked the jeep and we got out. Surely this was the northern most tip of the island and I couldn't help thinking that there should be a marker on the beach or near the entrance to the beach indicating as much. I had seen the markers place in the Florida Keys on a trip there. The Marker indicated that this is the furthest southern tip of the United States.

Eleuthera should have signs just like that. Tourist love it and eat it up. Just think of the photos it would generate.

Angela headed straight for the beach for a stroll while I explored the caves to the left of the beach entrance and went up the sandy path to the top of the area over the caves trying to get a view of the other side of the island from there. I wanted to see how to get to the many homes we say along that side of the island. I hadn't seen a clear-cut road so I needed some indication on how to get there. The beach was lovely. I returned there to watch Angela in the distance and dream a little. I knew that we would make up for loniness once we were in the pleasant arms of the Montagu Beach Inn in Nassau during the following week.. I was having more fun just being around her, smelling her sweet scent, touching, holding and caressing her at every opportunity and planting sweet kisses on her pink lips. I sat down on the beach and watched her bend to pick up seashells and other curious objects drifting in from the ocean. I thought of how divine she must feel in all this beauty and splendor she had witnessed now for the past several days. She was here in this tropical paradise far away from the small town experience in the cattle country of Los Angeles California. She was here with me, I here with her and together we loved it all. I myself had not enjoyed Eleuthera like this before. I thought that it's always a great idea to take time off like this and learn how to vacation in your own home. Besides there are places on this island where I have never been, little places of little significance, just heard of and that's it. I had learned to ignore the everyday challenges of my business and focus on Angela in order to appreciate what was going on this wonderful week we were experiencing together in Eleuthera. I wanted to know what the tourist felt and seemed so excited about when they visit our shores and now I was getting a good taste of that for sure. I felt secure and wonderful at the same time as I watched Angela in her black bikini bend over and collect the few shells in the distance and couldn't help but smile. The beach stretched on for about one mile in an east/west direction. It was brightly lit by the setting sun perched high in the western sky and shone with the radiance of a pearl. I was so proud of the nature God had blessed we descendants of the slaves with and felt that I could come back here again. Perhaps when Angela returns we can do this whole island thing over again and have twice as much fun as we did this time. Angela soon grew weary of the beach and shelling and moved toward me. She reminded me so much of my first girlfriend in high school, Jenny a Caucasian beautiful girl who was pale and pink and who taught me to kiss in the movie theater for the first time. Angela represented all of this to me.

We decided to move on. The sun was setting and there was not much more hours to explore this area before we had to return to Jane's Bay to catch those fantastic photos of the setting sun we hoped to catch. We soon piled back into the jeep and started back up the path toward the Haitian village we had passed through almost at the beginning. I looked curiously at the many side roads branching off from this path-leading west, which as where we had to go to see the homes built along the seashore by those persons from Spanish Wells. These roads were too narrow and grown up besides they were not navigable enough to be used by the homeowners of the area anyway. I soon came upon one road where the high-tension electricity wires were strung high upon the poles and followed a westerly road and knew immediately that this was the path I wanted to take. Along this path we were taken straight out to the water front after passing several wooden well-built homes that were well boarded up. This was no doubt a reminder of the terrible hurricane and how serious these people took that incident. There was a small stone path along the waterfront, which was used as a road. Although it was quite tough to navigate I took it anyway. We had nothing else to do but spend an hour or so finding our way back to Jane's bay so on we went. Along this road was a high fence enclosing the property surrounding three of the most beautiful homes I had perhaps ever saw. These homes were gorgeously built and stood high on top of a hill all lined off one after the other along this rough cement path which I hoped led back somehow to the main road. We stopped along the path to each of the three houses and took photographs and realized why this was such a beautiful place to build since it was right along the seashore and the area was so secluded and quiet. There was no one in sight of these homes the whole time. No doubt these were winter homes for some elite rich millionaires who brought the family out during the cold winter months to enjoy as much as they can of our grand Eleutherian sunshine. The water to the right or us along the path stretched out toward the horizon far in the distance, ahead of us in the far distance to the right was the dim figure of the island of Spanish Wells dotted occasionally with the white blemish of roof tops and the spotty image of various colors used by the inhabitants to paint the outside of their houses. The path soon came to and end and I soon realized that there was some dilemma ahead for me since there was nowhere to turn around. I soon, with some difficulty maneuvered the jeep across the path with my well honed driving skills and turned it around in the direction from which we came. We headed out in this direction relaxed with the knowledge that at least we knew now where we were going. Once back on the main path leading back toward the Haitian village we turned at the next right turn to further explore the area where these grand wooden homes were built. This was the area we had seen directly from the dock at Jane's Bay. These were the beautiful clusters of homes we had seen. The area was quiet and each yard was planted out with growing beautiful flowers, ungroomed which gave the impression that no one was living here at the moment but once the winter came the area would be busy with vehicular traffic and children and the other elements of neighborhood and family life that was characteristic to tourist colonies like this. I felt the time passing away as we turned from a dock area and decided to head back to Jane's Bay to catch the setting sun and take that photograph I had promised to catch thus further completing my collection of digital photographs of my beautiful island of Eleuthera, of which I was now so proud.

Slowly we backtracked our way down to Jane's Bay. Through the Haitian village again where a different clown was now wearing the line of clothespins across his face from ear to ear and looking like a reverse of President Lincoln and back along the dusty white road to where this little adventure had begun at Jane's Bay. The sun was now low in the western sky and partially hidden by some low-lying clouds but still shone through with that golden splendor which is so characteristic of a Bahamian sunset. I got out of the jeep pointed the camera at the golden horizon and pressed the shutter. I knew now that I had captured at Spanish Wells one of the most splendid sunsets of my collection. I looked back at Angela who was in the green jeep and smiled. I simply felt wonderful and for once in my recent history felt in charge of my world.

The Sun had set but the day was not over as yet. Savannah Sound had started their home coming the day before and I felt compelled to stop by on the way back from Bluff and enjoy as much of that home coming festival as well. Island life is quite slow so when the opportunity arises to enjoy something like a homecoming or a fair on the weekend or the holiday we jump at the chance, like other communities we spend countless hours listening to loud music, eating, chatting and standing around in groups chatting and drinking liquor until the wee wee hours of the morning when we are compelled to go inside. During these times we must come out and have fun. This is a part of the process of shaking of the harshness and sometimes drudgery of relatively isolated island life. The chance and need to get in the midst of the festivities was there. We would again enjoy it and enjoy each other together besides it would give Angela a chance to meet some of my friends and see the greater part of the Bahamian community here on Eleuthera and see how they acted and enjoyed themselves during these holiday times which are supposed to be the best. These are the best times for all of us and since summer has the most holidays of all this was the best time for Angela to visit. She had chosen unknowingly wisely. She would get the chance again to see my people in a festive mood. Besides the allure of the conch salad being prepared this late at night was too tempting not to allow oneself to part take in such festivities. Conch salad is one of the most flavorful and delicious dishes I have tasted. In the hands of the right chef it is simply divine with the bright citrus flavor of lime and other seasoning vegetable ingredients, pepper being the greater of these, a simply marvelous Bahamian creation. I would have to stop again with Angela as we did in Harbor Island and enjoy some this evening. The drive was slow and comfortable. Angela sat back once again to view what was left of this evening palette for the eyes and I drove on toward Savannah Sound.

Savannah Sound was nice tonight much as it had been for the last few years since they started having homecomings in this little town. This is the liveliest event this town has throughout the year. The park down at the waterfront was fully lit. The bright lights and the buzzing excitement through the air seemed somehow artificial for this place. People here were generally quiet and demure citizens without much to do about anything. Tonight was special and everybody showed up. Young and all, the sick and downhearted jumped up out of bed and put on their best duds and headed out for the park. It was much like the setting at the homecoming in the Bluff with the cedar stick stalls and the thatch that served to separate the stalls from each other and the customers from the goods within but it was bigger. It was almost twice as much people and much more activity. I couldn't notice that especially the bar it was a buzz. The patrons were lined on all four sides of the bar stall leaning and standing into it in and out ordering coconut water and gin, Anejo and coke, Kalik beer and all of the favorite drinks the islanders love to have on a holiday such as this. Many of us love to drink; drink and drink until we think we have had enough then drink a little more before retiring for the evening. We parked toward the center of the park then got out of the van to take a walk along the stalls in order to see what each one had to offer and quench our taste for conch salad, which was by now a busy stall among all these drinkers. There is a feeling among Bahamians that conch is an aphrodisiac that accounts for much of its popularity among the natives. The men especially like the myth and promote it so regularly among our visitors and brag as much as they can while gulping in bowls of the delicious salad. I don't know the science behind this but it sure does taste great. Angela got close up under me and walked along beside me as if we were really a couple. She was also looking for and anklet to replace the one she had lost during our trip from Harbor Island. She hadn't found one as yet and I assured her that perhaps she might find one at one of the stalls here. Around we went in the half circle that the stalls were formed in but we didn't find any suitable jewelry for Angela. We then headed back to the center of the stalls where we purchased some conch salads from the young men working the stall. We stood for a while and dug in savoring the lime and pepper getting a good dose of salad just in case tonight might be the night

Angela ends her dry spell, I would be ready. We then walked along a while sipping the juices and eating conch salad while looking out into the crowd and paying attention to the fashion show taking place before us on the basket ball court this time of the evening. Old and young women alike were dorning the latest fashions and making their way down the imaginary run way walking in such a manner to display themselves as the high fashion models of NY and other fashion centers of the world do. Much of it for the old women was humor. They strutted down the runway and did for more. The more laughs they got from a particular movement the continued it until the laughs wore off and some one new moved in to take over the action and move the laughter and the crowd along to the next event on the program. It was quite humorous and enjoyable in its small way and served to amuse the crowd and pass the time away giving everyone especially the inebriated that they were having a spectacularly good time. Many of my friends were there. Lots of people from Tarpum Bay, my home town and many from my old high school," Windermere" where next to this vacation with Angela I had spent the most wonderful four years of my life at boarding school among a fantastic population of human beings including the many foreign missionaries who worked so hard to keep the spirit of the school alive and unique. We were all brothers and sisters now in life and we all felt and knew it. We greeted each other now especially with hugs and other gestures of friendship and felt special in the company of each other. All because we had shared this unique wonderful experience afforded us by the participation of the foreign missionaries in duty and service to God. I greeted and introduced Angela to many of these during our wandering walk around the night compound of the Savannah Sound homecoming fair grounds. After wandering and finishing off the conch salads it was now time for another native delight thought by many locals to be another aphrodisiac, coconut water and gin. Simply delicious again it is another island blend of something unique and special that we have to offer the world. The water is sweet and smooth mixed with condensed milk and gin it makes a special delight for the palette. Angela loved the stuff and ushered me to the bar several times to sample this delicacy. We had a great time, standing around sipping our drinks and watching the makeshift fashion show which was still going on. Everyone was laughing and having a ball.

Immediately after the fashion show ended the Bahamian singing sensation," Nita" came onto the basket ball court accompanied with her two tall slim beautiful black dancers who usually accompanied her. These girls were so pretty. They wore a pink native print fabric about their hips, enough to cover them and about their breasts and shoulders, again enough to cover. These gals moved and rolled their bellies and hips to the calypso music Nita had produced, her own style and songs and were being prompted during the show by Nita to do various form of her unique native dance. They were asked to," stick and move", a contortion of the hips and belly. She was a beautiful girl herself. A native light brown girl, much lighter skin tone than her accompanying dancers, she too knew how to, "stick and move" a dance of her own unique creation. She had such a pretty smile. Her face was radiant in the harsh lighting filled out by the moon light and her fantastic dental line shone in the bright moon light as she sang and danced her way into the hearts of the mixed crowd there that night on the park in Savannah Sound. We had a great time sipping coconut water and gin and watching the fantastic show she had put on for us that night. After the show was over and we felt the weight of the coconut water and gin we decided to call it the night and left the few friends beside us at the park which would go on and on until no one was left to buy the alluring alcohol of which they had so much. That was the ending of a fun day. We had driven almost two hundred miles from the beginning of that day to its end and had enjoyed every moment of it. That day was so great; it stood out on its own so nicely. I would learn to treasure it and the woman who was with me that day for a lifetime. Quietly we drove home and were already in our minds preparing for the excitement of the next day ahead.

Chapter six

Saturday 11th of August
Islandia picnic

It was Saturday morning when I arose out of my bed. I changed and proceeded up to a sleepy headed Angela. Although she enjoyed the touring she seemed more and more tired each morning as it wore on. I upon arriving a Hiltons Haven met Angela still asleep in bed under the covers with the air-conditioning on full blast. I felt good about this however. There was no rush for anything. Wherever we were at any moment in time during the remainder of this next two weeks was just OK. There was no accounting for time and place we were free to do exactly as we wished according to our normal everyday rules. I had loosened up and made no demands for anything, Angela did the same. She just went along with me and enjoyed all that there was to enjoy. I felt good about that. I did the best I could to keep her happy and smiling she occasionally now tickled me in order to brighten me up and give me a feel of what it was like being tickled all the time. I shook with excitement at the touch of her hands all the time now and felt very happy that I had made this investment in her and glad too that I could give her this much joy. Angela told me about some of the things that were happening back home in Los Angeles California, she sounded a bit worried when she did and I knew that I had to do what I could not to let it spoil our vacation. Our kisses were growing sweeter and Angela was relaxing. As Saturday came I knew that our stay in Eleuthera was coming down to an end and I was glad then that I had taken so much time and effort to take Angela from one end of the island to the other in order to show her my universe and it magical elements. She appreciated this and assured me that we would have just as much fun touring California as we did touring Eleuthera. Some day, I didn't know when I would get that chance to see the beauty of California.

I sat on the bed beside Angela and caressed her as she awoke and watched her as she moved before the mirror undressing and dressing again after her shower that morning. She was ready now wearing her short black dress with lots of flowers in the pattern. The one that buttoned straight down the front. My genitalia hardened as I sat there and watched. I wanted her to get over her fear of where she was or whatever else was bothering her and just let loose. I wanted her love and needed her so badly. We were both in our own little world now, all she had to do was fall in my waiting arms. I was being patient and knew that when we were in Nassau together in the arms of the Montagu Beach Inn we would be able to fall madly in love. For that there was much anticipation in my mind.

Angela finished getting ready for the day. She always smelled so good and looked so nice to be around. I was thankful for her alluring presence. Today we had planned a picnic on a nearby lovely beach, the Islandia beach which was some four miles to the north of us before one reaches even half way to Savannah Sound. I had packed a delicious lunch for this occasion and since we had no accounting for time, it was now close to noon by the time we hit the highway on our way to the beach. Each time at the beach I had been doing some reading when I was filled with admiring the fantastic and tantalizing sight of Angela. The two books written by Bahamian writer Cheryl Albury and Michael Pintard excited and captured me, especially Cheryl. She gave me some insight from the book of what she was about, a busy lady so professional in a busy world and amazed me at the fact that she despite her lack of time had time to get organized and write such manuscript as she had. She had compiled a book of poetry and short stories that were fun and exciting, especially since she was Bahamian. I had glanced briefly at Michael Pintards book of poetry and knew from its complexity I would need more time to read it. I went on with Cheryl's book during those brief moments at the beach and at home day after day. I was loving it all.

We stayed at the beach at Islandia for some time that day. Sunning, bathing in the cool clear Atlantic surf and feeling the electricity in the air. We dined on ham and cheese sandwiches, native fruits, bananas and mangoes and drank wine. I then laid back on the sand, stretched off on my tummy reading the remainder of Cheryl's attempt at writing a collection of her works, both prose and poetry and felt proud to be apart of her acceptance into the writing world. I did meet her a few years earlier and felt some sort of kinship since she was such a nice person and such a beautiful woman as well. I felt happy that day since I finished reading Cheryl's book. It gave me more faith in things Bahamian and I thought, at least for the moment, that maybe we were getting somewhere as a people. Angela had been walking and collecting shells along the seashore as usual and was returning to stuff them into the wonderful navy-blue bag she had bought at Harbor

Island. I was not tired but a bit exhausted of the beach so we talked a while and played with each other for a while before getting up to leave the Islandia beach with the knowledge that another most beautiful day was almost ended. We drove home to Hiltons Haven in Tarpum Bay where I left Angela in order for her to get some rest and get ready for our dinner reservations at 8pm at Mate and Jenny's restaurant in beautiful Palmetto Point. Mate and Jenny's was a nice little tourist spot where guests from all over the island assembled for an evening of great dining and Pizza. Mate is a fun guy with a wonderful sense of humor who loves people and keeps them coming back for his wonderful kitchen delights. We would be there by eight. This gave us ample time to rest and attend to any other little details we had to attend to in that period of time. I had time then to briefly check my answering machine and email and get back to those persons I had to in order to keep the lines of communication open for when I wanted to get back to work. I knew why I needed to take this vacation but my customers on the island may not be quite so forgiving.

At 7pm I arrived at the motel where Angela was waiting in her room for me dressed in a white outfit and sufficient jewelry and accessories for an evening of good dining and pizza. She smelled lovely as usual and looked ravishing. I felt like the night was magical and could bring a few surprises. Mate and Jenny's was a great place to be on a Saturday night. The place was packed as usual and the waiter who was Mate himself was busy attempting to keep up with the orders as they came in from each table. We were seated by Mate in the far left corner of the room, which felt fine and were waiting for the menu to arrive. We hadn't had anything since our lunch on Islandia beach that day and were anxious to eat. The menu soon came as Mate passed by and handed them to us then we were off studying those menus attempting to find the best combination of pizza the restaurant had. I love meat, Angela loved vegetable so we chose a combination pizza, which I had had at Mates before and knew how good it was, so I was happy. Soon Mate came around after attending to a nearby table and we gave him our wishes for a medium combination pizza with a coke soda and a Goombay punch which I thought would be an accompaniment to a good few servings of pizza. Mate left smiling his usual pleasant smile and assured us that the order would be coming up as soon as possible. All of a sudden in the midst of waiting Angela began to sobber. She mumbled through her sobbing that she was feeling quite home sick and that she did miss her family. I couldn't at first understand this outburst of emotion in the midst of us having so much fun enjoying each other's company and the wonderful time we were having together at the various functions and dining opportunities. She went on with the fact that she didn't know how her family felt about her being away from them like this, that since she hadn't been anywhere outside of California before. She was feeling awful enough to cry after all my efforts to comfort her and make her feel like the special person that she was. I had spent all this money and time on this task and did hope that she could appreciate that. Now here she was crying. I then remembered what Angela had said to me several days earlier while changing in the motel room at Hiltons Haven. She said that her period had come down, that she was sorry and did not expect that to happen here while in the Bahamas and it was then that I remembered that many women suffered from something called PMS syndrome and attached Angela's sudden mild outburst of tears to this fact. She went on for a while feeling sorry for herself and her family back home whom she had call at every opportunity she got from my office phone. I knew that they felt satisfied by now about her where abouts since they did not call at all during this time and leave a message or anything of that nature on the office answering machine, not even her mother whom she told me was the most critical of all. Angela had let me know earlier that some of her friends were jealous of her being the one to be called on to take this fantastic two week vacation with her mysterious lover man in the Bahamas. She didn't let any of that bother her then but some of it was getting to her now. I watched her reassuringly constantly telling her that everything would be all right. I reminded her that she had phoned home already and that there was no need to worry about her family back home besides it would only be one more week before she would be back in their arms and there was no need to cry and worry like this at all. The surrounding guests around our table did not know that this was going on since Angela had cried quite conservatively and made no gestures to suggest that something major was wrong. We talked quietly as if we were just having a normal conversation and before no time it was over. The crying stopped, she dried her tears and all that was left of her little tantrum was her shaky mouth as she started to open up and talk with reason and come back to her normal happy self. I was so relieved that the crying had stopped and felt no sense of guilt that this had gone on at all. I tried to feel and understand her reason for being down hearted enough to cry and all I could come up with was that she was suffering some of the symptoms of PMS since there was no other reason for such behavior. I had never witnessed anything like that before in my dating career and felt as though I had had a first hand experience into something I had only heard about in the media and never witnessed first hand up to this time.

Soon after the tantrum had subsided the pizza and drinks had come to the table and I was ready to forget those few negative moments of the recent past. The pizza was as delicious as I had expected and we both dug in and chowed down while the surrounding murmuring and busy conversation of the surrounding tables carried on. The evening was wearing on. Mate had also ushered a native couple carrying a baby to the table right next to us. I remembered the lady as she had been a customer of my electronics repair business in the past and looked at her directly, smiled and said hello. She smiled back said hi and commented on the overpowering heat contained within the busy room filled with so many people without air-conditioning. I agreed with her then took a short break from the conversation to consume another slice of our delicious pizza laced with a new pepper sauce I had just tried for the first time. The sauce was the hottest thing I had ever tasted but it drove my taste buds so wild that first time I had to try it again to get that first unbelievable pepper high. Angela got brave soon behind me and tried some of the pepper sauce as well. Now I really felt sorry for her tender little mouth as she held back the pain and carried on as if everything was usual. The feeling in my mouth told me it was not. Kevin, an artist friend had told me about this hot pepper sauce, mistouk before and I did not believe how unbelievable hot he said it was. Now I had the first hand experience and had to believe him just now. We continued on until the pizza was gone finished off our drinks and sat once again, full this time, awaiting Mate to administer the bill for the pizza and collect the few dollars I had in my pocket. Shortly after settling down and relaxing with the moving crowd in the restaurant for a moment Mate came back over and gave us the bill which I reached into my pocket and paid promptly. I was delighted to have sampled such a culinary delight as Mate had served that night and I hoped that despite the hot pepper experience Angela did enjoy it as well. She was not complaining so I assumed that she had had as good a time as I. I customarily reached over to her, asked her how she was feeling, caressed her for a while and moved with her toward the front door of the restaurant where we observed the wonderful collection of photographs Mate had collected over the years and felt a special something for the one person of great fame I had met in my recent past while she bought fish in our village, Mrs. Pattie Labelle. Her autographed photo was placed high above the others her face shining with her resonating smile and I felt deep inside that this woman though famous and world wide was one of us. I remembered at that moment her great talent for singing and wished for more personal conversation with her instead of the informal instructions I had given her concerning which type of fish tasted the best of those from which she was to choose. I had suggested the hog fish file and felt happy enough that she had chosen to ask me this question as I stood beside her on the dock in front of the park at Tarpum Bay.

The night was dark outside as we walked back to the waiting jeep in the parking lot of Mates restaurant. Mate had greeted us as we were leaving and welcomed us back again anytime for a delicious meal when we preferred and I felt that I would return should I get the desire and feeling for great pizza and romance at anytime in the future. This was all apart of it I thought to myself and felt glad that Angela was finally happy again and feeling quite fine. We soon turned out of the parking lot in front of the restaurant and headed straight west to an area of town called," South Point." I remembered this place so well many times since being here so many times with my grand parents who lived there before passing on. They were gone now but the wonderful feeling was always there when I drove into south point past the lot where their now demolished house stood and that same feeling lasted while I drove straight out onto the gigantic cement pier which was an integral part of the small neighborhood of south point during those days and now. Being here this time of the night was special especially since I now had someone I loved with me. I had driven out to this dock so many times before and dreamed of spending just one romantic evening with a love of mine at least one time and now that dream had come true. God had given me my the wish that I had whispered so many times before, he heard me and I felt proud that he cared enough to fulfill even my dreams. We soon parked on the dock, which was now eroding because of harsh seas and hurricanes at its head some distance from us. Gigantic slabs of the dock had fell to the sea floor as rust had set in and destroyed that part of the structure. The setting was despite this romantic and I felt like a star sitting beneath the starry skies performing on a stage with my lovely girl beside me to whom I would speak sweet words to and change any doubt in her mind to love me and give me her all. All that she was and had I needed and tonight I felt like I could accomplish that task. Angela fell silent again just occasionally staring at me as we got out of the vehicle and walked toward a wooden reel table where I sat and took here in my arms under the starry sky feeling her warm body resting softly against mine. We were there for a reason and I needed to get this across to her. I had her captive, silent as remnants of what I was about to say to her formed in my mind and I sat there momentarily carried away with the situation for just a while until Angela began to sobber and tell me negative things again. I didn't give up on her however. Her doubt was brief and chemical she reassured me and I gave her all the grooming that night I had to give. I told her the deep things that I felt for her and refreshingly reassured her that everything would be all right between us. I did not look into the distant future unnecessarily. I thought of tonight and a little about tomorrow. Then much about the next week we would spend together in Nassau and felt comfortable about the fact that when these two wonderful weeks were over Angela would leave the Bahamas feeling that she had found the man for her in life. She would know that there was no other choice and no one who could love her as assuredly as I can. I told her all of these things and at the end she assured me that once she was over these feelings tonight everything would be fine. She had just needed some time. She then reassured me that once we were in Nassau the following week staying at the Montagu hotel things would be different. Just owe it to nature she said and by this time the crying was over. Once again she was comforted knowing that I had been patient with her and did not force her to do anything that she did not wish to do. For that she was grateful. I then felt a renewed spirit of love and concern for Angela and hoped deeply that this damn crying would subside forever. We kissed and held each other for a while, while at the same time rain clouds were forming. At this time small droplets of rain were forming and I ushered Angela back to the jeep just before the skies now partially darkened with clouds burst into a formidable amount of rain and soon this turned into a constant down pour while we left the dock area and headed for home. We took our usual slow evening drive from the dock in South Palmetto Point back to Angela's motel at Hiltons Haven where I escorted her to her room, kissed her goodnight then proceeded to my own room where I needed now to get some rest and prepare early the next morning for the next days events.

Chapter seven

Sunday 12th of August
Meeting Mom

The next day, Sunday was relatively uneventful. We started out for the beach a bit later than usual. I normally get started slowly on Sundays and today was no exception. Mom was up as usual in the kitchen preparing Sunday dinner and getting ready to meet Angela whom I had invited to come over for Sunday dinner when mom returned home after her Sunday church commitment. Dad was at the airport as usual at the taxi stand waiting for a plane to come in around noontime so he would not be joining us for Sunday dinner. We had a fabulous time. Mom had prepared a delicious meal, Peas and rice, macaroni, coleslaw and young steamed mutton from the Symonnette farm in Rock sound. It was just fabulous. We talked and ate for at least an hour, Angela and mom particularly. I could tell that mom was fond of Angela. She was the type of girl she wanted for me and as she had indicated when some of the other girls from town came to the house to bring their sewing. Mom was the best seamstress ever to hit the island and she had a growing business in sewing that had lasted many years and with this career she had been able with the help of my father to educate us all. They did do well at this task. Out of the six of us kids all but two of us were educated in American universities abroad. One of us reaching the educational achievement of medical Doctor, the eldest boy; this was an achievement for which I was rather proud. We dined and talked on until about 2pm in the afternoon.

Angela was happy to meet my mother, my niece and nephew who were at the house at that time. She had met dad earlier on the telephone. According to dads report of the conversation, which took place in my absence he was excited almost as much as I about her coming to visit me. He did mistake Angela for a daughter of a similar name living now in the east coast region of the United States. Dinner that Sunday was fine. I was glad to bring someone new into mom's life that she could appreciate and deep within I knew that mom approved and wanted Angela to be apart of my life as much as I did. She was continually teasing me about the fact that at twenty-five it was time to get married. "Life is short," she said and relayed to me that she wanted that joy and experience of marriage for me. Today was one of those days when I couldn't agree more.

Dinner ended with our formal good-byes until next time. Angela gave mom a big hug and assured her that she would be back in the Bahamas the next chance she could get which at the time seemed like Christmas time so they parted and separated with that. Angela and I headed for a beach I wanted to show her on this one of the last days she was to spend on the island of Eleuthera. Tomorrow would be the last opportunity to tour and see more of the beauty of Eleuthera. Off we went after Sunday dinner to Half Sound beach. A wonderful white sandy beach half way between Rock Sound and Tarpum Bay. The road again was quite rough but we navigated it due to the fact that we really wanted to see the beach and spend the remainder of the afternoon doing what we now loved to do, sunbathing and dipping on the clear blue ocean waters. Half Sound is on the Atlantic side of the island and is every bit as beautiful as any of the other beaches we visited but is a lot narrower due to the fact that the landscape does not allow the outlay of a broad beach. The terrain just prior to the beach is quite hilly not allowing the flow of the cool Atlantic waters onto the beach side terrain. There we lay the whole of Sunday afternoon with the whole beach to ourselves, undisturbed reading the remainder of the books I had purchased at Island made both of which I did finish that very day. Angela really relaxed that day and enjoyed Half Sound beach. By now she had spent one week walking the beaches of Eleuthera enjoying the scenery and collecting interesting souvenirs of the island she had now come to love. Her promise that she would return to visit me during the coming Christmas vacation quite nicely told me how much she had enjoyed my treatment of her and the island itself. For just the announcement that I was happy; she made me feel quite warm and loving inside toward her. I felt happy also for the sentiment she had expressed toward me and my fair tropical paradise. Sunday was now to a close after our many hours on the beach that day. I had won a few triumphs that day. I felt most happy that I had consumed the work of the two Bahamian authors I was introduced to earlier in the week. The town of Tarpum Bay was quiet that evening as we drove in near to sunset. Church was in progress at many of the denominations in town. The grand structure of the Methodist church quite fully occupied with its usual evening service in progress. I simply couldn't wait for the beginning of the day to come.

Chapter eight

Monday 13th of August
End of a Lovers dream

Monday was quite an uneventful day. Both Angela and I got out of bed late having had a prior busy week and wanted to rest up sufficiently for the fantastic week ahead, which we both were excited about for various reasons, mainly our occupation of certain hotel rooms on the island of Nassau. Monday was meant to be a relaxed day during which I took time off from my devotion to Angela to pack my suitcase and make the necessary arrangements that had to be made for our stay in beautiful Nassau. Around noon that day I met Angela at Hiltons Haven sitting and ready to meet me for our drive to my bank in Governors Harbor. We took the slow drive down to the bank in Governors Harbor Angela was quite relaxed and familiar with the wonderful scenery along that Bay front drive. We talked and smiled our way down the shore until we arrived into Governors Harbor in front of my bank where I withdrew the money intended to sustain us during our stay in the busy metropolis that was Nassau. After my stop over at the bank we drove to the Blue Room once again where we had a wonderful lunch then drove back toward Tarpum Bay where we would spend the day getting further ready for our trip into Nassau. We settled all bills with the Motel owner, a beautiful peace-loving lady of great vision who had served the island as a nurse for the government health ministry for many years until she earned the money, which allowed her to construct the Hiltons Haven motel thus realizing her life's dream. To this day guest come to visit the motel and its owner from all over the world including countries like, England, Germany, Canada, Japan and many more exotic destinations. One thing is for sure; she is a great asset to the tourist industry of the island of Eleuthera. Now Angela would never forget her and like the others would have a home to come home to any time she pleased. Return visitors on an annual basis were one of the pleasant things about business at Hiltons Haven. I had met many of the guest who had stayed at the motel and one my entertaining interests is to meet these guests when they returned from time to time to the motel year after year to spend a few days with the owner and get the rest they needed to carry on their command of that part of their world from which they came. Other than these happenings and my work on the island I was at times during my tenor on the island quite bored. Therefore I needed this vacation with Angela in order to do just what it did, excite me and revive my love for this great tropical island on which I live.

During the drive back to Tarpum Bay I remembered a very popular tourist spot that I wanted Angela to see before she left the island. That site is the Ocean Hole in Rock Sound. This hole and inland lake like hole over 100feet deep contained on all sides by a strong limestone wall the hole sits oddly in the middle of town. This hole is filled with various varieties of fish and has been a tourist spot on the island for some decades. The fish love being fed any food items visitors can afford to feed them. It is quite an interesting sight to see the scores of fish surfacing menacingly to recover the bits of food thrown overboard to them by the visitors. This event create a brief havoc as the schools of fish race to the surface in a race to out do the others and have all the bits of food to themselves. Seeing the varied colorful species of fish in this movement is quite a unique sight. I have not seen anything like this naturally in any other place of the world. We drove into RockSound that afternoon and ended up in the center of the village where the Ocean Hole is located. Angela immediately found it to be a lovely and unique sight. Her face broke into a broad smile and she stared down at the fish as they came up to the surface to swiftly take in the bread thrown over by the few other visitors that were there. This hole is also a popular swimming place for local residents although no one was swimming today. We are told constantly that there are no dangerous fish in the hole and that it is quite safe to swim there at any time. Its a wonderful sight to see the community boys jumping into the hole diving, swimming and generally having a great time while swimming among the harmless species of fish. We had great fun at the hole meeting the visitors who were there, a few couples visiting the island. The couples were diving enthusiast and took off while we were there out into the and around the perimeter of the hole along the limestone walls covered with barnacles from which some species of the fish feed. The couples told us that they often frequented the island year after year and always stay at Edwina's place, a local beach side motel known for its tranquility and great food prepared by the owner Edwina Burrows. I enjoyed meeting the visitors, I knew that I would perhaps see them the next year when they were down then we would have something to talk about. Shortly after our adventure at Ocean Hole in Rock Sound Angela and I were back at Hiltons Haven where we planned to spend a quiet evening having dinner on the patio outside and talking, relaxing and generally having a great time in anticipation of the day to come when we would board both ourselves and our jeep onto the mail boat and be transported over the five hour trip into the city of Nassau where we would be spending the remaining glorious week we had together in a splendid way from which we never hoped to awake. Angela up to this point proved to be quite a good companion. Angela was loving and considerate, friendly and compassionate, I loved her for being just that. I knew that the next week in Nassau would be a fabulous and fruitful one for us both. Angela was not sad now since her episode Saturday night. She was brave and now at home by my side and I did all that I was able to make her comfortable and at home here in our tropical isles. I loved her for being the person she was.

Chapter nine

Tuesday 14th of August
Mail boat Journey-Nassau

This was perhaps one of the most wonderful days we spent together besides the day during which we took the day trip to Harbor Island. I was feeling magical. I looked forward to the days ahead of us in Nassau although I was saddened by the fact that already one week had passed and Angela's vacation would be over in only one week from now. She would have to leave the Bahamas and go back to her ordinary life in the mountainous hills of California, I would miss her dearly as we have grown closer together in this short week and I feel more deep feelings for this girl. At this point I am delighted just being around her. She has turned out to be good company and someone I can talk to about anything that is on my mind. What a great relief and a state from which I do not want to return. Angela has given me the freedom that I was seeking. In her I see a friend, which I can have for life if I wished. Her pleasant, kind demeanor has taken me and she has given me the same freedoms I have extended to her.

During the open hours of the day Angela rested at Hiltons Haven knowing that we would be leaving later that afternoon on the mail boat the, "Eleuthera Express." The journey by the express would take approximately five hours. I had taken this journey by boat several times before and had come to love mail boat travel. Once aboard the boat in the afternoon at 2:30pm the boat finishes her off loading of freight and the mailbag then sets her course for Nassau. It is quite a pleasant experience. The ride is not fast but fast enough to feel like you are getting somewhere. With that big engine vibrating underneath all of that steel you are filled with the strength and the power enclosed in that space down below. The large new boat move steadily and surely through the seas cutting its way, crashing into and overcoming the waves and seas ahead on the journey into Nassau. After what amounts to a good rest and lots of fresh salt laden air, if one ventures out of the passengers cabin above deck especially high up onto the second floor near the captains steering quarts, one is refreshed and invigorated with a total ease of mental burden and allowed to totally relax and enjoy the journey since there is nothing else to do. You must always provide your own entertainment, normally when traveling alone I bring a good book which I am currently reading and get a great sense of accomplishment from the quietude and restfulness of the journey into Nassau by sea.

So the afternoon came. At noontime I took the jeep to the hotel at Hiltons Haven and there we exchanged pleasantries and good byes with the owner, Nurse Hilton then off went to begin our sea journey into beautiful, exciting Nassau Bahamas. It will surely be an adventure for the souls aboard. I have found sea travel much more relaxing than then the tense moments spent in crowded airports and much more tense moments hanging on to dear life in the thin layers of air above the earth. Air travel just does not compare to the pleasantry and ease of sea travel. For one the boat is much larger and more spacious than just the one little confining seat in an airplane. One can move about the cabin at will and do anything he or she wishes at will without the tense restraint of the captain and the airline stewards. On a large boat traveling at good speed traveling is wonderful and relaxing. One has the option as well of bringing along their favorite books, games, stereo is wanted and there are many other options which make travel by sea so much more relaxing and pleasurable than air travel. Besides all of these options travel by see costs only one quarter of the cost of air travel. Since it is not the first choice of the masses it is an uncrowded option for those who favor this mode of travel. In addition to all of this we were able to take the jeep aboard to use as transportation in Nassau while we were there. All these options were pleasing to me and I smacked Angela gently on the lips as I drove down the high way toward the dock in Governors Harbor for the long pleasant ride during which we would be fed by the cook on the mail boat, "Eleuthera Express." Angela seemed reserved and did not pass judgment on the suggestion of journeying to Nassau by sea. We arrived at the dock as planned made arrangements with the Captain to board and take the jeep along among the busy bustling of the crane uploading and off loading freight for the many people and truckers on the dock at Cupids Cay. After which I assisted Angela along the gangplank aboard the large green and white vessel that would take us graciously and smoothly into the well lit crowded night harbor of Nassau. When we reached Nassau it would be 9pm in the evening, there would be time only for offloading the jeep and making our way to check into the hotel Montagu Beach inn during the remaining evening hours then settle in for a good nights sleep and an exciting adventure which proved to come for us the following day. My excitement was heightening. We would have another great week together before Angela was scheduled to leave the Bahamas and once again we would enjoy each moment of each others company along with the amusement mother nature and the environment provided. We both knew that Nassau would be quite different than the tropical rural beauty of Eleuthera Island, which we had come to appreciate and love. However we would make the best of the crowded city landscape and cherish it for all that it would give us, wonderful days and nights together in an attempt to love and be loved.

The mail boat roared on through the seas toward Nassau. We had lost sight of land and were now in the middle of the Caribbean Sea headed in a west northwesterly direction toward the ship-laden harbor of the capitol city Nassau. The slight vibration of the aft engine and propeller drove Angela and I out of the crowded passenger cabin and onto to the second floor captains deck where we took cushioned seats in the cool afternoon sea breeze just in front of the captains look out windows. The small navigation crew busied themselves inside setting the course and engines for the trip and making the necessary radio transmissions and preparations for the journey. I always feel renewed after one of these open sea journeys and look forward to each time I get the chance to travel in this fashion. This journey by sea was so much more pleasant. For the first time I had a companion who was not some stranger who I had just met and broke out into conversation with. Angela was the person whom I had spent a whole close intimate week with loving and taking care of, nurturing and caressing at every turn in order to comfort her and make her apart of my family in order to win her love and all the pleasantries that go along with it. I felt a great sense of calm as we sat and talked for hours as the cool sea breezes caressed our bodies bringing with it the cool light refreshment we both needed. Our journey by mail boat was going fine. For hours we sat there looking out at the horizon expecting to see at the closing moments the shape of an island, any island peeking its way above the horizon and out of the water to be claimed by the eyes and wished to be Nassau. For other moments we sat quietly staring out into the bright blue sea as it raged against the sharp hull of the express cutting and crashing through the water like a knife sending the resulting salt spray laden air up aloft and into the faces of the passengers who took the journey as we did above deck. The journey was magical. The freshness of the sea air renewing. The long journey allowed one to reset the internal clocks and set pace for something new. A new entry into which one came but did not know quite how they would return. At times I missed the quiet tranquility of Eleuthera and felt the grave depravity I felt when traveling to Nassau and other places beyond. I needed Eleuthera and it quietude for my mind. The pleasant pace of life and the coping of the trying landscape like the sea brings a barren refreshment with which I identify. The long hot days, the cool sometimes-dreary nights bring with them a drugging and slowing down of the mind that is most relaxing. This pill effect is the essence of paradise. Some time away from the work a day world back into nature where only mans primal needs are of the most concern. Not bills and traffic, not crowdedness and people, just hunger and sleep, rest and privacy. Only the essentials are needed for daily survival and not the pressure filled mundane processes brought about by the financial pressures of the day. Eleuthera is simply magical and it rests you with its charms and coves, its hiding places to which one can withdraw from the public view.

Our journey continued steadily on into the evening during which we witnessed another glorious sundown. The sky was clear, the sun bright and large as it streamed deeply into our eye peeping at us and dying slowly beyond the horizon far into the west. There we were in all of this, just there. There was all of this and nothing to see. The glories of the moments had overcome us and we were swept aloft in the state of rest where we quietly needed to be. Above board each man reserved, waiting, watching wanting and not wanting for this restful journey to end. Finally after much conversation among us and with another couple visiting Eleuthera from Nassau for the homecoming weekend it did. Far in the distance we spotted the lights peeking out of the water staring up into the sky as the many islets leading into Nassau Harbor were seen. The captain slowed the vessel down at the sight of these and began making preparations for his cautious announced entrance into the much-visited Nassau Harbor. As we cruised in along the islets our fellow passenger, Mr. Deleveaux pointed out the names of the many islets and told us stories as to why these days they were so brightly lit. The harbor and the bright lights of Nassau were now taking shape. We had traveled from one world into the next and now the bright glares of the many streetlights, to numerous to count were telling. Already the mood was being set. The surrounding passenger above deck exclaimed the many first things they would do once on land in the nighttime metropolis for which we were headed. I felt deeply inside my nerves tighten though not as tight as times past when I was alone on this voyage. Today I was a bit more relaxed and felt much better, this relationship with Angela was telling.

Our captain signaled and occasionally brought his bright light to rest on some obscure little sail boat traveling in the dark distance to the east of us or at times to the west of us, obviously they were not following the established rules of night time sea travel. Our captain was a safe steward of his ship. The harbor was a fantastic nighttime light show. The golden glares of the many lights ashore on Paradise Island to the right were surprising. Each time I enter this harbor I am amazed at the many luxury yachts and powerboats lining the entrance and docks as we pass along the overdeveloped shores of Paradise Island. Each slip is filled with sailboats and ships of every size and description. It is difficult for me to believe and except that so many people in the world can afford to dock and spend so much time crowding the Harbor of our little island metropolis. The towering hotels on the far Atlantic shore of Paradise island stand most visible above the relatively small condominium complexes dotting the falling green landscape of the island once known as," Hog Island." I am always amazed at the magnitude of the city that I consider small and crowded after being away for so long. The narrow mouth of the harbor quickly turns black under the glare of the bright lights and before you know it the Express is ready to dock and end its journey among the many dazzling, dancing bright city lights of which I could not take in enough. At times like these one is totally absorbed by the dazzling sensation of the moment. These bright lights and this dancing crowded harbor are the first sign of things consumed in this powerful little seaport. In the distance the gigantic cruise ships loom in the distance, towering above the water line like the tall towering hotels brightly lit and lively as a flotilla of loud party boats with their loud calypso music and drunken dancing passengers drifts ghostily by in the cool night air as the captain attempts and shouts out to the linesmen on the docks in an attempt to bring the large vessel so powerful to rest.

After docking the vessel there was no rush to go anywhere. We sat and waited along with others on the top deck of the boat as the many vehicles were off loaded to waiting drivers excited and anxious to head for home and complete the night with a glorious bit of night rest. The green jeep was soon off loaded and we made our way down the steel painted ladders, which led to the main deck. We got our luggage from the first mate at the compartment in which it was stored and preceded to the jeep to make the drive to the hotel. I paid the captain the fee for delivering the jeep to Nassau took the keys and went ahead to load the luggage for the remainder of our trip. Soon after navigating our way off of the Prince George dock and on into the light night traffic on Bay Street we headed east. The Montagu Beach Inn is a short drive from the dock so it did not take long to make the drive and end up at the front desk with wallet in hand in order to secure a nice room for the remaining week until the following Monday when Angela would fly back home leaving me lonely and restless again. The charming night clerk assured me a room on the third floor. She took the credit card, made the imprint and handed me the key for the room after taking a ten-dollar deposit for the key. I thanked her then proceeded to lift Angela's heavy suitcase and other bags onto the elevator, which we boarded with the entire luggage and made our way up to the third floor. The room was nice as most hotel rooms are. The large glass door over looked the entrance to the harbor and the broken down site of the old Fort Montagu hotel who's glories were long past a remnant of yester year and glorious times past during the Bahama's turbulent by gone era. I felt quite happy to be finally that night in some comfort. The television was soon turned on and the air-conditioning turned up to full blast in order to quell the sticky warm night air, which filled the room. The weather was still warm and Nassau with its crowdedness is known like most cities to carry much more heat then the family islands of which my Eleuthera is apart. Soon after I made the trek back down to the vehicle in order to collect and bring the remainder of the luggage into the hotel room. I had packed a large green suitcase with more than a weeks preparation of clothes for me. No telling what Angela had packed in that heavy ass suitcase of hers. I will say only that I had seen a few delights and hoped deeply inside that there were a few lovely good night teddies store inside. From this close proximity I had hoped to end Angela's dry spell and be entertained by her night manner and daily dressing which when watching I enjoy so much But for tonight we would rest. The journey though nice and restful left us drained as it wore on into the night and I was anxious to make it under the covers and hold Angela close to me for the evening. We soon did make preparations for the evening. After Angela was finished with the bathroom I took a long shower, brushed my bright pearlies, readied myself for bed. The thudding deluge of the brown air conditioner mounted in the low left corner of the room. It had been a wonderful day I thought and landed on my pillow with a head full of sleep for the night.

The night passed quickly by. I slept like a baby, like I had not done since coming to Nassau alone so many times. I was comfortable tonight and felt a real sense of security and calm as I lay there. We arose the following morning filled with excitement and joy.

Chapter ten

15th of August
Waters of Nassau

The remainder of the day was great. Angela and I took off from the hotel at around ten o'clock that morning and headed west on Shirley Street toward the western of the island. I had lived in Nassau six months ago and was excited myself to see how it had changed. I had heard many rumors that it had changed and wanted to see the changes first hand. West Nassau is a particularly magical part of the island. West Bay Street runs for about ten miles and serves as the gateway to some of the most exclusive areas and homes on the island, the end of which is the world famous Lyford Cay. There are so many exclusive hotels, restaurants, condominiums and elegant private homes along the route west. One is simply dazzled each moment of the journey by the splendid designs of the buildings and the attention paid to by the home and business owners to make their particular location unique among the mass of such exclusive buildings. The crowd ness of all these quarters is simply astonishing. The simple fact that so much attention is paid to owning a unique location is overwhelming. No two buildings are alike; all of these dwellings are simply beautiful and stand out one after the other. A tour like this is recommended to anyone visiting Nassau for the first time. Angela sat beside me in the jeep fascinated as we made our way through the dense morning traffic. We soon passed through the business centers in the middle of the island and made our way out of the center to the more dazzling residential areas of West Bay Street. Certainly one is taken aback by the splendor, the gigantic investments and the attention to detail home owners in Nassau take in constructing their unique space in which to live and enjoy life in the busy tropical paradise. West Nassau is certainly an exclusive area where property values are inflated to reflect the intention of the neighborhood to remain exclusive. Most of the persons living in these neighborhoods out west are businesspersons and certainly persons of quite enormous wealth. We didn't see the smaller average looking homes that we were accustomed to seeing during our tour in Eleuthera. The homes we saw in Nassau were in another category. The opulence of even the front lawns leaves the beholder in a transfixed bewilderment, in a dream of playful fantasy, the fulfillment of a wish. We both sat still gazing from one side to the other as we passed along the grand white walls and the manicure front lawns until we reached the round about near the golf course at GoomBay beach near the popular Crystal Palace hotel. This area and the property of the Crystal Palace hotel is one of the most beautiful I have seen in all my travels. The extent to which the have beautified even the roadway with a manicured tropical garden filled with clean cut grass bordered with some of the most exotic flowering plants and shrubs one wanted to see. We certainly took the sites of people exercising, taking morning strolls and crossing the street from the parking lot in order to get to work. Angela sat in amazement and quiet wonderment as we made our way along West Bay Street. We were simply sight seeing at the moment and had no goal in site as far as a place to go. We had time and were simply for today taking in the sights learning to relax and enjoy our time among the busy environment of the city of Nassau. If all on Nassau were as comfortable, beautiful and serene as West Nassau there would be no blemishes on the island at all. The problem with Nassau is the overcrowded, cramped residential neighborhoods where three quarters of the population of the entire Bahamas lives. Not all of the residents of Nassau live exclusively as the residents of West Bay Street and the other neighborhoods of, "Out West." Some of the neighborhoods are infested with drug dealing and crime; these are the ones we had to try to avoid. These neighborhoods are mostly located in the center of the island of Nassau and are the present structure of the old city of Nassau, which has expanded beyond all of the expectations of the old generation. All of the cheap affordable housing sought out by illegal immigrants and those who cannot afford the present day market rates is located in these old beaten down neighborhoods and should be avoided should one wish not to take unnecessary risks in travel.

Our tour of the western area of Bay Street went fine. There are many sites to see out in the western district of Nassau and one should take sometime set aside to see this wonderful lively display of good living along the western waterfront. The many lively colored condominiums and hotels make the trip memorable. Areas like Love beach, Compass Point are particularly fascinating stretching for miles and filled with the exquisite residences of foreigners and financially welled healed Bahamian hosts. The real exclusive area is Lyford Cay, which is located in its own-gated community a short distance from the end of West Bay Street. Lyford Cay is the famous residential community of Movie Stars and the financial giants of the world. They boast of the inclusion of residential homes owned by people like, Sean Connery, Sidney Poitier, Peter Nigar, Sir John Templeton and many other world famous personalities wishing as they have for a place to simply forget the outside world and live in their own community of peace and absolute splendor. They have achieved this in Lyford Cay. Our tour of Western Nassau took us several hours of driving. We ended up at the end of the tour in the Southern district of the island in the residential neighborhood of Carmichael. Here we drove on through the middle class environment of small new businesses and the neatly painted homes of the working class people of Nassau. These are the neighborhoods of those persons formally living in inner city neighborhoods. These sprawling residential areas of Nassau are the result of the motivated working classes of Nassauvians who moved out of the run down inner city neighborhoods, which still live on in infamy because of their being crime ridden and almost unavoidable location. In driving from one part of town to the other it is impossible to avoid passing through these dilapidated neighborhoods. These crime-infested neighborhoods are guarded and patrolled by the police as closely as they are able to. Obviously I did not frequent any of these neighborhoods in my attempt to show Angela only what was beautiful and positive about the city.

Later in the afternoon, after lunch and toward the end of the business day Angela and I drove east. East

Nassau is much like the Western area in that it is filled with exclusive residential neighborhoods only. The dramatic difference is that mostly successful Bahamians own the opulent homes. It is simply a wonderful sight to view the success of most of these residents living in these exclusive areas. Some of the more memorable areas out east were, Dicks point which is a waterfront community bordering the main road as you drive through the extreme eastern shore of Nassau. The area is blessed with a beautiful beach where members of the community gather during the evening hours after and before work to workout and exercise, some of them bath in the wonderful Bahamian surf and sun. We had truly wonderful times during our week in Nassau. Nassau is fun. You simply relax in your hotel room, order room service or order out whenever you are ready for something to excite the taste buds. We really had a wonderful time exploring Nassau and each other.

The following day after a wonderful nights rest and a morning of fantastic excitement Angela and I toured the one place she felt she had to see before leaving Nassau, "Crystal Marine Park." The Theme water park is a lovely island unto itself filled with many wonderful salt water exhibits, a restaurant and a small hotel for the liking of tourists that love water parks. We parked our jeep at the foot of the bridge on Arawak Cay and walked across the one car only bridge to the water park community. From there we purchased tickets to the park from the main booth at the foot of the bridge and entered the turnstiles for a morning of viewing fun among the theme water park sites. Angela had never seen such a display anywhere in her travels in the west near California. She desperately wanted to pet the dolphin, feed the sharks mentioned in the brochure and have a chance to tour the underwater tower visible from the main road on West Bay Street. Angela simply had a wonderful time viewing the many water animals on display at the park. We talked, laughed and had a wonderful time holding hands and feeling the undulation of the day as we strolled from site to site. The magnificent detail of this exhibit is astonishing. Almost every species of underwater creature in the Bahamas is represented in the water park. They have a live shark tank displaying several live species of Shark. Also displayed is a wonderful collection of various stages and species of sea turtle including the near extinct Hawks bill turtle and the loggerhead variety. There were numerous artificial environments where entire cultures of species were cultivated and presented in glass cages for the entertainment of visitors to the park. We not only had a wonderful day but we learnt something about the variety of sea life abundant in Nassau and the Bahamas. Angela felt exhausted after our walking tour of the sea marine park so we headed back to the hotel for some rest and relaxation during which Angela rested and I called friends in Nassau to say hello and that my girl and I were in town.

Chapter 11

Our wonderful, experience is ending

During the Remaining time before she returned to Los Angeles Angela and I continued to explore the small picturesque Island of Nassau, New Providence as it is officially named. We visited many wonderful touristy locations and beaches, which I remembered and frequented when I lived in Nassau some six years earlier. I couldn't allow Angela to miss the beauty of Cabbage Beach, Paradise Island. A two-mile stretch of glistening white sand adjoining various world famous hotel properties like The Atlantis Hotel and several others. My triumphant retreat to my Family Island home, Eleuthera, was one of the more adventurous experiences in my short-lived, until now, uneventful life. In relocating to Eleuthera I had given up my chances for the fast paced career offered to many growing professionals like myself in the Cities of the world. I was seeking solace, a place where I could retire from the uncontrolled, stresses of the modern day world. I remembered in times of extreme stress periods in the crowded, relatively isolated city my peaceful existence in my Eleuthera Island home and longed once again for that communing environment with its free easy going people. I loved people and missed the daily close contact and free association with them as I had on the Island during my childhood. Eleuthera lends itself to this ideal, living daily in communion with its other inhabitants and visitors is the norm. Personal interaction between the Islanders, they have so much free time to devote to their personal lives, was an ingredient I missed in the cities in which I had studied and lived. I craved that personal nourishment and free association more. After relocating to the Family Island of Eleuthera that realization was realized. I, with some difficulty assimilated with the local population and the benefits were tremendous. The long cool days of winter, the long, cool breezes of summer nights in the midst of a loving native community brought back the emotions of fulfillment I sought. I was resigned to giving up my dreams of the grandeur and success of a modern engineering career for the arduous task of rebuilding that career in the Family Island and in the process assisting with the development of the Island and its people as a whole. As one can imagine this is not a goal easily realized. It would take many years of personal sacrifice of the modern numerous amenities the cityscape has to offer that the relatively undeveloped Island does not have and it would mean that my days would be spent in the learning and contemplation of just how I would go about having this great impact on a settled, reserved environment and people as those who reside on these Bahamian Family Islands like Eleuthera. The challenge was irresistible and once realized would be the realization of a lifetime personal achievement and goal. That struggle goes on even until today. Angela's visit with me was tremendous refreshment and a sanctuary into which I could sit for the short while she was here and the possibilities of her joining me here on the Island was a great promise to which I could hold and look forward to in the future. Her passive, quiet, caring demeanor were welcome and through her I had derived at another milestone, one of having met the lady of my dreams; a lady with which I could have a future marriage and look forward to raising a family, perhaps the greatest eventual goal of them all. As we look to the foreseeable future we must see to provide for the future generations the freedom, tranquility and economic means by which to carry on the noble Traditions of the Eleuthera Island culture. As Nobel prize winning poet Derek Walcott alluded to the fact that the Island people in several regions of the Caribbean exist in relative obscurity uninfluenced and untainted by the sometimes perverse nature of the industrialized world. Their existence need not be sanctioned by the outside world in order for them to appreciate their existence.

This would be such an achievement, such an elusive goal, definitely something to live ones life for, to apply ones energy for that greatest of imagined goals. Together we can get there. As I always say, "The mountain is hard to climb but through the sea of challenge I will swim with unfailing with the goal of the enlightenment of my people in mind." Another notion for which I strive, "If a fish splashed in the far flung regions of the Caribbean Sea, would anybody hear?" A voice for the people and the land of the Caribbean must be attained.

Now that Angela had arrived I had a sabbatical from this tradition of mine. Myself along with her had relaxed to the fullest during these few days of glorious discovery and intermingling. We discovered a world which was foreign to us but one in which we knew we could live forever, a fruitful passage into a world of desire from which we never hoped to return. That was our wonderful journey of discovery, these few days. Only time would tell if Angela would be willing to make the ultimate sacrifice and move to the island to be with me permanently. Time did tell. Love was not triumphant that day. Island life can be lonely at times without the attainment of the desires of your heart. I await my ultimate loving interlude with the final passionate, loving stranger I hope to meet. Until then my Activism goes on.

"If a fish splashes in the far reaching regions of the Caribbean sea, will anybody hear?"

George Major

Love's Beautiful Stranger

Just at a time I had not suspected, that beautiful Angel came.

Tonight is Friday night and so far the week has been usual. Not really a drag but I can't stop thinking about Boganskia and how she has gone. Just picked up one day and decided to go to college. It's been a few weeks now and I am constantly thinking of her actually becoming a hairdresser. She could do something different, she could study to become an accountant. Something with a little more depth I say rather than a hairdresser. Hairdressers talk too much. They stand around all day with those plastic gloves on, waiting on a sitting room filled with talking women, talking, laughing and catching up on the everyday happenings in all of their lives. Seems a bit idle to me and they can't make that much money doing it here on the island. There are too many of them already and relatively small and it is difficult to make a livelihood at it. Couldn't she have become an accountant? At least she could've studied bookkeeping or something a bit more relevant than hairdressing. I wonder if she'll be cutting men's hair. The thought of her cutting the hair of other men shudders me; I die a little bit inside knowing that she might meet some other guy that way. I don't want her meeting some other guy.

I've loved her from the day I first saw her there. She walked so closely past me, so beautiful. Her yellow eyes captured me in an instant as she rolled her head silently in my direction, as she walked by the van behind her family entourage. She was tall and slender, long beautiful golden hair, bright and pretty. Her hips trim and honest like those of a fashion model in touch with herself. Just what I was looking for in a women at the moment and there she was close enough to touch. I knew of her but had not been this close to her before. This was certainly the first glimpse and she had my attention all the way. I had to have her be mine.

I had thought of her before and knew that she would be this beautiful. I've known her older sister since we were in public school together and she looks fairly attractive with her flowing long black hair all the way down to the small of her back, and her light brown luscious lips that set off her dark brown eyes. Even she might have moved me but on a different day. Her younger sister had it now and she was working her stuff, looking better than Cindy Crawford or Naomi Campbell because not only was she that attractive, she was right here. I had never thought of her in this way but because she was right here in front of me I couldn't help it. I hadn't seen anyone this attractive to me in months. In the distance the entertainers at the cultural event went on with their native dance, so many of them moving across the floor in their bright colorful costumes.

That's why I'm so disappointed today. I know she has to live for herself and is trying to be independent and strike out on her own. She's a young modern girl whom I hoped would want to know me more and depend on me a little more. I didn't mind. I had thought it through and it seemed like a good idea. Can't do much about it now. She's across the waters in the big city, Trinidad, without a word or my advice; she's gone, just up and left me dangling in the wind like a lost man without recourse. There is something to get excited about however, it's Friday, the weekend and Caesar's place is having a party. There'll probably a chance to meet somebody. See more of the beautiful young girls in the village and get some happy feelings back again.

Today is the beginning of something new. I'm making a new start. The perfect opportunity to get started living that happy carefree life I've wanted for some time now. This evening I will dress in some nice duds, have a few drinks with some friends and possibly meet some of the new guests in town; that's always a thrill. Meeting someone new and possibly making the contact I need keeps me going for a while. It gives me the next boost, obviously Angela didn't do it, and aside from her charming good looks she had no depth. She turned out to be unimaginative and much afraid of taking in this intelligent new stranger in town who wanted to rock her world.

It had been some time now since she left town herself but the memory of her lingered on. One knows that if she had tried we could've had a beautiful love affair, which might have lasted forever. That's how attractive she was. Her long straight face with those piercing yellow eyes and that soft brown hair swept back into a pony tail really did it for me. She had a curious innocent stare which made me believe that I could teach her all of the tenderness I know and we could grow together like two beautiful doves hovering above life, with all the love in the world that we needed.

I had shed my tears and wiped them dry. Sobered a bit, felt lonely for days without the occasional glimpse of her and by now felt fairly confident most days that I could go on living having known that I loved her with all I had. For a long time now after getting over the bitter hurt that was Cherelle. I was able to love again and I gave it all to her, every chance I got near her, whispering sweet things in her ear that would make her smile, calling her on the telephone for those unexpected long searching chats. Trying to find out whether or not I was getting through the fog in her mind. Making an attempt to show her things about love that she could not see. I had tried and failed but not until I had shown her all the love I had to offer, all I was willing to give to make our lives fruitful and better. For some reason I would understand later, a lot of money and a runaway love affair were the driving forces behind her leaving our quiet little waterfront village. So I cried my tears for a while and today I was willing to get up and move on.

Actually I had not felt this good in a while. I had taken my shower, soaped up gracefully in this tropical climate in the most fragrant body gels I have. Green on green would be the chosen outfit for the evening. My brother had chosen the shirt for me from some outlet store in Carolina where he lived and the pants, a velvety smooth material, pleated and freshly ironed, were lying on the king-sized bed just above the black boots and the lucky silk socks I save for such occasions. Right Guard is good, after slipping into my soft green golf shirt I apply some of my fragrant talcum powder, which is really a great sensual thing for me. And I end up looking quite stunning, tall and muscular in one of the twin body length mirrors before me. Our little world is out there waiting and I can't wait to be a part of a nice evening affair during this festive holiday Easter season.

I get out there on the waterfront in front of Caesar's place and see that the crowd has gathered for the evening celebration that is going on inside the small seaside restaurant. For the moment things are relatively quiet; cars are passing by going north and south, one or two occasionally stopping outside the restaurant and sneaking quickly inside for a delicious snack, probably crack conch, which Caesar's place is so famous for. There I am standing in my shiny black short boots feeling like Guy, a far-out friend from Trinidad, and looking over the crowd of beautiful girls standing in groups talking away as if no one is noticing.

Paul from Harbor Inn, a small resort up the street, has come over and whispered that he has some guests coming down soon whom he'd like for me to meet. For the past few weeks Paul has been introducing me to all his guests. He is somewhat happy to know he has someone close enough as a friend to whom he can introduce his guests to and leave them for a while to converse and exchange pleasantries and the like while being entertained by someone with the local flavor; one who takes interest in and enjoys meeting strangers and turning them into friends for as long as it lasts. There's really nothing like meeting total strangers and after one long pleasant conversational information exchange, feeling good enough and as comfortable with them and them with you as if you have known them you're whole life, and they are a part of you, and that here in Lovely Bay this is their home if they please.

So for the time being I am standing waiting on a cue from Paul to walk over and meet the few white guests he has with him, who have just appeared from up the street. In a moment, I realize there are three of them standing beside Paul by the lamp pole near the parking lot; two women and one man. They look quite pleasant, comfortable enough, and seem quite happy and intrigued to be among our local community. After what seems a long time Paul looks toward me, signaling me to come over and meet the wonderful guests he is gracing us with this evening.

Paul can be so formal at times, he makes me feel awkward as if there is only one way to do this and that he knows exactly how it should be done. Sometimes he's really a bit too rigid. I follow him to the lamp pole in hopes of being relaxed and conservative enough to entertain Paul's guests and hoping to have a chance to meet the tall one who is for the moment in conversation with a hooligan I know from a settlement down the island. A pretender whom I wouldn't wish to see her turned over to. For a moment I am angry that he ever got to know her and hope that nothing develops from their brief unadvised encounter.

I am introduced to the remaining two guests Klaus and Helga, two remarkably friendly German people whom I find out shortly are married and quite happy, and honored to be here in Belmaral Island and Lovely Bay with us after a long tiring flight from Germany. They had arrived just a few hours ago before they were taken to Harbor Inn to meet Jennifer and Paul, their host and hostess. They love Jennifer, the owner of Harbor Inn, and so far have been having a great time exploring what little of the scenery we have here on the waterfront in Lovely Bay. They exclaim that the water is just gorgeous and that they can't wait to do some snorkeling, something that they've come all this way and waited so long to be able to do. I am happy for them.

Just then I look over at the lady dressed in pale blue denim who is ending her conversation with the guy from up the island and see that she may be someone, at least she looks like someone who may be able to replace Boganskia in my life. She may be someone who can get rid of some of this emptiness I'm feeling or may be able to put a smile back on my face, and do something for this heart of mine that needs some doing. Maybe I'll get the chance to meet her and since she is not married perhaps she is alone. If she is alone perhaps she is also in relationship limbo. So since she is friendly enough to take some hits from the guy from up the island perhaps she is open enough to my charm, if I am in good form.

She is almost ready to come over, and I can't wait. Paul gestures to the attractive lady with the long blonde hair that this is his friend George whom he would like for her to meet. I extend my hand to her with a pleasant smile and say, "Nice to meet you, Angela.", and she reciprocates with a smile and an extended soft hand which I gently take into mine and apply the necessary pressure to get a particular friendly, "I would like to get to know you better," feeling across to this gorgeous mature white female. I make no bones about liking white females; they are particularly attractive, and much more pleasant and conversational in nature than most of the local girls I know. So I go after them every chance I get and hope to meet a nice one with the openness it takes to start an exciting relationship and a new experience in life which may lead to who knows where.

So over she comes now, a little reserved, to talk some more with Paul and catch up on the local happenings and get into the groove of island life I suppose, and try for the moment to meet a few people who will make her stay as comfortable and as pleasant as we are known for giving our visitors down here in this part of the world. And on I go talking with the German couple, Helga being quite radiant and beautiful with those flush pink lips and cheeks smiling back at me, and Klaus the computer expert, fairly interesting in conversation, going on about life in Germany and how happy he is to be here for a vacation.

We talk for a while when somewhere in the context of the conversation I am told that Angela is from Miami, Florida and I exclaim to her, although we haven't talked to each other yet, that I could use a friend in Miami. So maybe by now she is picking me up, I really want to hit it off with her. Eventually we do get to talk to each other and I find her quite conversational and friendly. She loves friends and expresses that she enjoys people from other cultures, like mine, then I exclaim to her that she is quite liberating for me at this time. She's all smiles during our long conversation and seems very interested in a friendship and getting to know someone new here locally. She goes as far as inviting me to come over to Miami for a shopping trip. But for now I decline because images of that black guy from Barbados getting burned alive in north Florida flash through my mind. I've spent too many sleepless nights in hotel rooms alone in Miami and Ft. Lauderdale to take her up on the offer right away.

"There's nothing like meeting a local," she says, "who can take you around to all of the right places to get the best prices when you are purchasing." She was now high on "Gemini Hardware," my business for which I had on occasion to go into Florida, especially Miami Beach, to purchase hardware goods for resale. She seemed quite receptive to me, and the idea that I could end up in Miami Beach with this gorgeous woman really eased my mind. If I could build on our relationship during the two weeks she was here and take her out on a few nice dates getting to know her, I may be able to kiss those succulent red lips before she leaves the island and heads back up to Miami, where I might meet her sometime in the near future. The fact that she has her own house helps my thoughts a great deal. She's attractive, vibrant, so well-traveled, why is she alone?

For the moment I didn't care about that. What mattered is that I met someone that could fill the big void that needed to be filled in my life. She could do more for me than any of the others I had been trying to approach. After our brief encounter I already felt that she could do it for me. She let me know that. She volunteered to take me around when I came up to the States, and she agreed to act as my purchasing agent in Ft. Lauderdale and do whatever she could to help me along in my business, which was great. I felt comfortable with her. She understood me when I looked over to her earlier and said to her that I could use a friend in Miami. It was the way that I said it and she knew what it meant. She could tell that I felt the tenderness in her personality and saw the look of intent when she looked back at someone, that I had seen her intention in getting to know me. Obviously she had gotten the deeper meaning.

This perception of her told me that we were on the same wavelength. Her concentrated stare and cozy smile as she smirked when she talked told me that there was something here to be discovered and that I was the man for the job. I was charming and intelligent. There was a lot for us to talk about, my college experience in the States some years earlier, my need to expand my contacts and experience in South Florida in order to accommodate my business venture. Her body, a tall physique in those tight jeans, gave her away; this was an exciting woman on an adventure. She was probably looking for the things I had to offer, such as tenderness and the ability to entertain her. The next two weeks were going to be exciting, I thought as I savored the tingling sensation running like electricity all through my body.

I did not know how old she was but I assumed she was at least as old as I was, thirty-three. She was very mature and certainly older than twenty-five. I didn't even care about her age, although I was curious. She did mention that she had visited the island seventeen years earlier with Steven, a friend who sailed his boat down here as often as he could from Florida. She had met Steven in a bar in Florida and they had sailed down to the island here for a vacation, along with a group of friends. Fair enough for a woman who had literally traveled around the world. She had been to the Pacific Islands, the Far-East and Hawaii. Every few years, she explained, she would leave her job and take off on a new adventure somewhere around the world. She liked the tropical islands of the world in particular. She had been fascinated with the islands of East Asia, and Borneo specifically, as she had been there twice. Boy, I thought, if fate ever gives me a chance with this women with her sense of adventure and my desire we could really make a great team. We were both uprooted, portable and ready to go to adventure and intrigue.

I know what that's like, taking chances. That's how I got here back on the island after living in Trinidad. I had gotten a chance at a new and exciting life. A life that so many city dwellers craved. The perfect, quiet island life free from the stresses and the crime that the city had to offer, and it was bad in Trinidad. Each day the news was filled with reports of shootings and robberies, no good news it seemed. Someone was always dying for one reason or the other. I didn't need that. I wanted an environment, which I could live in peacefully, be happy in and raise a family, taking each day at a time and as its own. Living slowly was my desire and up to now things were going great in that regard. Island life was relatively happy, stress-free, and as long as business went well everything was fine. I wanted a good life and thought that maybe I could share some of this island life with Angela for a while at least, until we really got together and I proposed to her. Then we'd get married. All I needed was to find out if this excitement we had was for real, did she really like me as much as she appeared to? Or was she some former, world-traveling hippie looking for her next short fling? She seemed pleasant enough and none of these descriptions matched her. I was positive toward her and couldn't wait until I could ask to take her somewhere to enjoy the remainder of the island alone.

I see her after a few days on the beach. She is smiling and happy to see me. We talk briefly, after which I ask if she went on the hill to see the aunt she asked about earlier in the week, whom she knew and remembered from her previous early trip. My aunt didn't remember her. We sit and chat for a moment and again I'm tingling inside and floating, actually enjoying the conversation and her facial mannerisms. She reminds me of a pretty comedian I know from the comedy channel and I feel like I've known her for more than a while as we have been on the same wavelength since we met last Friday evening at Caesar's place. She describes her beach exploration and how beautiful and quiet the beaches are here and I am moved to get even closer to this beautiful women who is all alone like me here in paradise.

The next morning I call her up after she has had breakfast and invite her to go for a drive that evening. She agrees and I pick her up at 7:30pm. and head on out to Rock Sound, just eight miles south of Lovely Bay. The settlement of Rock Sound is the capitol of this area and one with a few more scenic attractions to offer. We end up at a small restaurant Edith's Place, and take a table by the window opposite another table filled with a noisy bunch of South American tourists shouting, laughing and having fun as they all sample the local cuisine.

Surprisingly she is not hungry so I order something to eat and she just orders a beer. I can see then how she is able to keep that wonderful tall thin shape in those tight pale blue jeans and how she manages to keep such a youthful appearance for a forty-two year old woman. Yes, she had told me her age on the beach, during our brief discussion and I couldn't believe it. She didn't look a day over thirty. Her skin was tight and young looking, smooth and not a wrinkle in sight, and I saw that she had put on some rouge to lighten up the color of her skin. She hardly wore makeup the other times that I had seen her. She was beaming with natural beauty from head to toe and I'm not sure she was aware of it. She was casual, easy-going and wonderful to be around and converse with. She knew quite a bit of what was going on in the world around her, including technology, my favorite subject.

The following morning I closed my business down for the day, business is slow this time of year anyway. These great times are sometimes far and few between so why not embrace them when they are here and enjoy the pleasure of a hot moment close to someone you are growing to love? Why not tingle and twist with delight on days like this with this tall delicious doll that had entered my life, with no end of possibilities?

After breakfast was over, I stopped by and met Angela waiting for me on the patio just beside the restaurant at Harbor Inn. She was dressed casually and I could see that she had packed a few things in a knapsack to take with her on our North island tour. The day was beautiful and sunny, without the extreme heat. She was oiled down in some sweet scented suntan lotion to protect her skin and curled up on the seat next to me while we drove, talking and looking at me the way I wanted her to…

Slowly we make our way down the winding roads of the long narrow island. The road travels along the seashore right next to the Caribbean Sea. The light blue turquoise waters are breath-taking and something one can never get used to. The view is always changing, the tide, the wave action, the cloud cover, all elements, which always makes this scenic drive a pleasure. Angela and I both love it. I go slowly up the island past the small villages in-between and we pass some landmarks for me to point out. We head up to Turtle Island, the popular lovely tropical island with its mysterious coves and pink sandy beaches. We've come about 70 miles, and we finally stop and have lunch in a waterfront restaurant overlooking the yacht harbor. We spend the afternoon conversing, taking in the views at Turtle Island and sipping on tropical drinks until it is time to make our way back up the island south to Lovely Bay.

The next few days are great. Angela and I spend lots of time together, mostly in the evenings after my work is finished for the day. She tells me what she did that day and we discuss life and the possibilities of what may happen when I come over to Miami on a business trip later in the year…

The remainder of the two weeks has gone by so fast. I can't believe what fun I've had with this pleasant woman. She has really made me feel like a man and I respect her for that. I'm going to miss our days together when she leaves tomorrow. I am a little bewildered and I'm trying to get over that feeling that I'm losing someone again. She tells me she has made reservations and plans to come back to the island during the summer when she is not teaching so that we can spend more time together and get to know each other better.

We promise to keep in touch by phone and the mail. I'm shaken and cannot bear to see her leave as I kiss her good-bye at the airport the following evening.

Life goes on; we write, email and call each other from time to time keeping in touch and planning the next time we can be together again...

Detached in Mother's care

In the silence of the afternoon
When no one else is near for miles away
I can depend on mother.

I see her rye, bitter taste, bush medicine like
Leaving hammers on the doorstep
Giving chores at a drops notice
Calling for supper to the herds heaped on the grasses.

Nothing freely in this, this is family
The bittersweet pride of mothers having after their
sons on a sunny day
Cannot say why but a single man wishes she'd call
more often
Sheer delights when mother calls.

Even the notion of her being near
Eternal fervent care is what I call it
No other notions enter the enterprise
Mothers must go sometime.

Away she went to Nassau, today
She left me with the treasure of knowing that
Saturday she'll be back again
Not too far away, time enough to hold on
Mama's boy I'm not, though I hate the dose of
medicine
I cannot hope but think this is family love.

A mother's care if sure

Standing firm in the crowd when your in trouble
Somehow mothers know
To coin a phrase, "I'm the notion of mother's milk
Grasping holding like a straw and drinking cool"
Mothers know the answer to every dream
And fill you with their own sometimes.

She can convince you that the world is wrong
And change your mind in a minute to her foolish
notion
She has the power to cure sickness with a handshake or
a smile
That's the power of mothers
Ordained and carried out with missile-like precision.

ISLAND LIFE

George Major

Jabim

Lime juice, crushed ice, sugar, fresh spring water, make it Jabim
A poor man's enterprise indeed.
I went to America and ordered some lemonade
They gave me a comical mixture of tart fancy liquid so foreign to me.
No real citrus at all.

I love my Jabim, maybe the folks in America don't know
Some of the wonders of the village man's sober mind.
Things like Jabim on a hot sunny day in the middle of children's getaway from college The greatest refreshment they will ever know is Jabim.
One sip on a warm summer day sends one's palette scurrying for more.
This refreshing light dessert is drawn by buckets
Cooled in iceboxes and cherished by the working public.

Firstly the lime juice, not any lime juice will do
Give me the freshest key limes in the factory.
Lime green, bright green and stingy to the touch
Near bursting and ready to jump.
The process of harvesting these limes is history itself.
How the master sits up there in the clouds
Raying beams of energy to these green, sour limey delights, is history.

Sour limey is a flavor, like no other

The bright sharpness in a single lick is enough
To send an electric beam to the brain that will never be forgotten.
A wirey post so large that millionaires never forget its charm.
In America they use lemons, call it lemonade, no such thing for me
Give me the sharp, sweet concoction we call Jabim.
Sharp and refreshing enough for any fancy man
To deliver a dance in the early wedges of the afternoon.

Poor in enterprise, rich as farmers who cultivate this limey gift in quarters
Reserved for the unknown traveler on this mystery ship
The key lime on a tree breaks out in blossom during the early spring.
Charmed and blossomed by the honeybee
Another link for the honeybee to win over adversity
The key lime is groomed at the feet with spring water so sweet
Jutted up from the tight spiraling limestone, the sweet pleasant rock
With alkaline enough to poison a pig, sweet pleasure you have there.

After grooming the kidney of the lime tree,
Spread throughout the village like hog plums,
The season for picking, a few a day is near.
The key lime harvest is slow.
Slightly ripened fruit from this tree is a daily task, perhaps it was made so.

Each home in the know address a key lime tree with its own regard.

After a few years of blessed sunny summers the harvest draws near and one is able to Collect a daily reward through the key lime factory growing slowly Swiftly delivering on time these magical delights.

Key limes are not only for Jabim however.
A variety of ventures capture this mealy chitnik with a flavor so sharp
It can make a blind man see golden streams of wiry magic.
Try the limey key on fried fish, maybe on a cured lobster salad during mealtime
In the middle of warm winter before the catching season ends.
Try some of this lime juice on conch salad
The aphrodisiac of the Caribbean native knowing full well
That the wetness of moisture is sense, do it well.

The key lime pie knows no limits, its useful to the imagination in that sense
It recreates its sour, tart delight wherever applied
One can only imagine the possibilities.
Take for example a tequila ribbon
Where would that be without the key lime and its sharp condition?
Power enough to break any matter of palette and taste.

The key lime pie has been around for centuries, many have partaken in this delight,

Too bad now we can't get members to use the original key lime flavor
Instead using a powdery manufactured delight, a near comparison in pies.
Along on the ride through history the key lime has been one of the favorites for drinkers Wishing to quench a thirst or crack up a boring afternoon
Jabim has been the answer, get to know this
And join in the magical enterprise long time now a mainstay
Of village islanders everywhere in the Caribbean.

Sugar cane juice, crystallized or juicy fresh
Add a magical spire to the subliminal tartness in a key lime.
I used to lick it raw for the connection, the wiry, darting specialty inside.
The conch on a summer's day applied with lime juice and saltwater
Is a special delight not had by many.
The rubbery softness in texture, and the calm nutty sweetness of the conch
Draw out the flavorful magic of the key lime.
Powdery reflex in the conch mixture is a great comparison to nothing you have ever had.

So now back to Jabim.
I've never had Jabim for breakfast.
Jabim rhymes with the sun and riddles itself inside the mind
The moment a notion sweats the worker's path.
Clip on the moment and anyone with a lick of Jabim

Wants a swallow of the wicked, tart hazed captured in a bottle,
Cooled under summer trees in the fields of the hostile accompanied worker
Weaving the fields of subsistence humor on an island as wide as the eyes can see
And as primitive as the imaginations of its inhabitants,
Imagine well and know the fruits of labor.

Jambim is an institution, where was it discovered?
No! You can't tell from gleaning, history can tell the only story of Jabim, can you hear?
Jabim is glorious, perhaps the first palatable discovery of a housewife
Taking a trek through the woods on a summer's day
Feeling lonely, despised and rejected
And then it appeared, the green flesh in a pocket of solids, musing and amused, fat Bursting with a delightful candor unknown before her walk into the woods, maybe.

The joy of Jabim is endless, taken with fisherman on outdoor excursions
With the hopes of having lunch before the day ends.
Holiday workers, troughing in a delightful gaze, the boss man crying,
"Time's up boys, let's go home, let's push!"
Some hear in the not-so-distant future.
Jabim has been discovered on many shores of the Caribbean
Perhaps a natural progression we have been given,
You know a code through which to identify oneself,
Jabim may be like life

A creation out of a creator with endless possibilities.
A myriad fancied by kings and angels since the turn of the century.
Why rant and rave about this delight?
There's no other to match its potential
Once you've known Jabim you can't go back,
The knick-knack enterprise of fiddlers jiving has something to say in time.
So do the magicians of the Caribbean, they have something simple to say.
Something uncomplicated and new, who's fresh to this enterprise?

God makes miracles for all.
I'm just saying he gave us our Jabim
So that we might have something over America to route in our direction,
All cannot travel, you know.
Need comfort of the mind that life is unique
And a treasure in simple things like a magic drink one cannot get
In the middle of Manhattan on a midnight gaze to the Theatre District.
Get Jabim while riding a simple dock, leering at the bright midnight stars.
One has to fight the world, stay back the magic and know his place forever.
Don't go out with the heady miracle workers,
Stay home and spin your miracle candor in the presence of the almighty man himself.
Enjoy a gullet of Jabim and know that life is real and true.

He gave us this, no one can take it away, not in name
or in fancy.
This one is ours, direct from the streaming rays of
sunlight afoot on our summer's day.
Though we can share, give them a hop, a mixed lolly
prize,
(Whispering, out of view) — "Save Jabim for the
masses."

Living on the Edge of the World

Living on the edge of the world where Columbus
brought Isabella's dream.
Where Atlantic Oceans pour endless streams and tar
onto lofty white beaches and drift into the cove.
Where gigantic lanterns far beyond the surf give up
their debris,
At the edge of the world so green, still so untouched by
human care and nature.
So natural and shy the landscape rolls along,
untouched by natural disguise.
The pristine flavour of crisp clean air that sweeps aloft
into summer breezes
Flowing into the gentler side of solid green masses
Freely flowing far in the distance, the landscape.

Give us back our land or do you wish that
we sit upon the tar-filled beaches and cry out
to heaven for the land? Should we stay at
home and focus more sharply upon the lonely
imagery of Ashanti warriors angrily emerging
in full dress with spears and shields, emerging
from the bushes where they've hid for
centuries? Arising now they protect our
generation from the shadows of portholes
near and far beside our crystal wall. Do not
hide from me the right their passage passed
from them to me. Give us their prize that we
might run their race to its end.

We've failed in so many ways to see the
gleaming side of home. We all are dusty,

failing to provide their bending backs with pride. We live as well we know but failing in our mark to freely give us that which is of our own.

Now to those pinioned upon the rocks of innocence beneath the still perch which cannot move, we share with them this cup which we will pass, just slightly alive but fresh with thanks unto a master we all know by name. Lord, open up to us the labour that kept us through the years. Allow us to sip the coolest water in the evening beneath the great big cedars in the slow and drifting breeze of summer. Lord, grant us our wish to possess our land.

The Beauty of Abaco Built

The lines are fine, the finish smooth,
except the joints indented be.
The bottom round and smooth.
She's small, yet large as she should be.

Row Roe, go softly with the tide.
Slice and slide atop the shifting glaze.
Take them to Governors and ports, and fishing
grounds.
Take them to heaven if there you be.
Show them how well your blues and reds are shifted
atop the bubbling, bright white layer that shows you
well.

See the proud and beaming eyes that gaze you,
Show them how fine they too can be.
Stay new and jointed, shaped and shiny.
Flow into the hearts of those who dare to see.

George Major

Has Paradise lost? The Future of Eleuthera Island in the Bahamas

An essay on the future of Eleuthera Island, Bahamas Greetings. It goes without saying that we are having a great sunny day. The weather is fantastic, our friends in town drunk on our exotic fluids and the procession of the dead a memory for those of us unaccepting of abysmal, undocumented nightmares we perceive the journey to be. We do not always rely on the scriptural account that God will deliver us from the evils of the world, taking us safely from this world into the next, if we believe. Safe passage into the unknown future.

With this behind us we move on to the pleasantry of fun in the sun, or we shall see.

This time of year is particularly interesting. The majority of people are back to their self-employed jobs, those of us who have them, the others left to the task of filling our days with some meaningful means of earning an income. This has been an ongoing institution in these Bahamian out-Islands for centuries. With little resources provided for organized capitol development Islanders, like others in remote portions of the world, were left with the task of earning their daily bread. The two most popular methods of doing this in our environment has been fishing and farming.

Long ago our ancestors were relieved from their original assignment in these archipelagoes and abandoned to both survive in an unfamiliar environment and forge a pathway for future generations of their Afro-Bahamian offspring. The unforgiving landscape and undertowing bountiful ocean were the two major sources to which these then-new Bahamians would seek their physical nourishment. So out of this application of themselves to the land many amateur farmers and fishermen were born.

After generations of driven, necessary, daily trials some affirmed patterns emerged. The land could provide vast amounts of pineapples, tomatoes, sugar cane, yams, sweet potatoes, sweet peppers, onions, coconuts, mangoes, bananas, cassava, thyme, spices and other delightful forms of food both for trade and for the subsistence of the family groups.

Likewise the sea gave up small frying fish like snapper, yellow tail, jack, school masters, grunts, tarpum fish, sea turtles, conch, welk, shad, spike, bone fish, hog fish, grouper, porgy, crab, lobster, Spanish lobster and countless other varieties of edible species which provided the back bone of the diets of waterfront communities in our Bahama Islands.

Trends emerged soon as island fishermen followed and verbally recorded the migration and seasonal schooling patterns of fish like the Jack fish (June to November), the crawfish, the Nassau grouper and other delightfully unique species to our Caribbean region; lately with the invention of the modern sea craft, dolphin (mahi-mahi), marlin, barracuda, tuna, mackerel and other exotic fast-moving fish are caught. These trends both in Agriculture and Fishing soon brought about dependable annual seasons that the Island farmers and fishermen could take advantage of in order to supply other inter-island markets with the plentiful bounty of fish and farm produce. This led to

141

the temporary street stalls and market atmosphere still existing in many island cultures both in the Out-Islands like Eleuthera and in the city of Nassau.

With God and nature providing our daily bread and fish, and the odd animal penned and sacrificed for food, a sustainable pattern began. Without outside assistance or foreign hands to interfere, the island was able to go on at a self-determined pace. They regulated daily life themselves for many years went on in a post-innocent approach to self-preservation. Thus the familiar reference to Island life being, Â'laid back.' There was nothing to rush for; the land produced at its pace, the sea gave up food in an almost predictable regular pattern. A rhythm of life emerged; this pace governed Islanders, setting the overall pace of life. The Island environment, led by the process of nature was indeed laid back. Islanders were interdependent. Communities were so closely linked out of necessity that they chose to live in close quarters in order to be available to each other when the need arose.

Islanders housing and communities were formed in groupings called settlements. On our Eleuthera Island there are about twenty of these. The settlements are scattered from the Northern tip of the Island to the Southern most tip, each settlement separated by a recurring, measurable distance of eight miles. Someone must have governed this and had plans for such separations.

Modern life in Eleuthera draws on the past. Like the old way of life in Eleuthera modern culture relies on both the land and the sea, however in a much more limited manner. The aspirations of islanders have changed. The dependence on nature as its vital driving force has changed. Yes, nature still exists in its splendid form but the application and attention or focus on nature for subsistence in no longer as much of a need — or is it? The modern Islander is influenced by external forces, the international media, national governmental reforms and regulation, the encouragement and association with generous tourists, foreign homeowners and other travelers, and these influences take their effect.

All of these factors and more bear on the vulnerable psyche of the islander. The pressure to conform to the global lifestyle is a most prevalent force among islanders these days. Through the educational system, church, work and other associations islanders are encouraged to abandon the island, because of its lack of modern economic, educational and financial resources, in order to get the most enlightened education and earn as much money as possible; indeed live out the same life, adapt the same potential as your counterparts elsewhere in the world. This notion is both troubling and good. While generations of islanders have attained these previously only imagined goals the effect has been a massive and terminable draining of the people resources of the islands. To this factor the islands have seceded once again. The futures of these islands primarily due to this draining effect are in jeopardy.

To date less than 10 percent of the original islander descendents remain. Scores of the young and middle-aged seeing the economic potential of migrating elsewhere left the island leaving only those behind who have either an established business or a governmental appointed position on the island. Our islands are lean these days. The bountiful resources of the human being have been replaced with the yearning desire of many to relocate to more fertile economic shores. Those that remain enjoy the uncommon quietude and communion with nature and the clear blue sea, but are burdened at the same time with our very existence, our future as a vibrant, self-sustained people. We that are left behind bear the eerie effect of a victim who has been robbed of his dearest, most meaningful possessions. Although life must go on, the break-up of the most guaranteed unions of the human family are troubling. We are left bereft and mourning the loss of our sons and daughters to the viles and vices of the foreign outside world. No telling what the safety of a loved one is in the heart of a brutal New York or wild-paced, out-of-control city like Miami, Florida. There is much to be concerned about here. The iceberg has been tipped; which of the flotilla of our idealism ships will sink beneath our feet next?

We are in the throes of an unrecoverable situation. Having cast our bread across the waters we are out of reach of those crumbs of the human womb to re-gather them and bring them home to a triumphant, resourceful existence in our islands. We must say goodbye to our lost loved ones to the world; laying the blame only on our own ignorance and lack of foresight and strength as a people to gather ourselves and fight with fervor against the wild influences of the outside world. Our Garden of Eden has been violated and we are left to pay the earthly eternal cost. There are those who are able to look with us in pity at our great loss. The extent and proportions of such losses are not yet assessed, just newly realized.

The shock to the system has just set in; we are caught with our proverbial pants down as the industrialized world has run away with our dearest treasures, our children. We are left unable to gather the strength to bear this burden; still shaking in this unfamiliar, unsecured environment without a clear understanding of our future. This Island, Eleuthera has much to ponder. Indeed we have been left to ponder? Our cityscapes, like Nassau, Freeport, and newly-formed Abaco Island continue, like the outside industrialized world, to attract our most productive, ambitious islanders to their competitive, stylized sweat shops. We are powerless to resist the emigration of our peers and offspring. There is little alternative, not very much we can do. Where is our strength, our reprieve? When will we rise up and resist this alarming trend? We must, before its end, resolve to find a real solution to this trend. We are depleted to the last 10 percent. Those are not good odds are they? The blood has already been let; now sutures and doctors must clear this anemic wound.

There is a solution I might suggest that has for so long been the foreseeable solution, but not adhered to by Central Government and interested foreign investors. There is a model constructed in outer communities, a complete self-sustaining solution evolved, tested and proven in the industrialized world. That solution, like nature, is the construction and development of a complete economic ecosystem. This economic ecosystem must have resources in place to sustain its progress. Isolated elements thrown into the economy to appease malcontents are effortless and have in the past proven damaging in many ways.

Isolated hotel developments controlled by Government appointed cronies, a practice of the previous Administration and once the lifeblood of our island, are but a stick in the mud as far as a total solution. Man shall live by more than bread on the island. Man shall live by sustaining a secure, comfortable environment and future for he and his offspring like other industrialized areas of the world. We must use more than our ecological, tropical environment as the answer to our economic plight. Investments in us, our people, is the most direct answer, to provide the non-enlightened masses with the resources needed to see the future potential of themselves and our lovely island in a sustained manner.

What we need in these islands is a complete functioning economy with the resources, people, and systems in place to provide the necessary sustainable backup in order to drive the system. We need a multi-layered educational system; a varied resourceful industrial environment, not just jobs for the needy but professional career-oriented jobs with a sense of purpose and future. We need a capable workforce in this place we call home. An educational system to feed this career-oriented work force will be the answer to our brain draining over the many generations; it has gone on too long unchecked. Through the significant investment of stable, sustainable capital investors the potential of our island can be realized. Through the complete cycle of career, education, social stability, personal investment, ongoing family, and other applicable human initiatives the rebirth of our island, Eleuthera, can be realized.

We must continue to petition Parliament, our most visible source of much needed economic measures. Government must know that much is at stake here, and to count the lives that we have lost. How can we continue to feel comfort in that? Displacement or the relocation of people is a most troubling sign. This trend will have to discontinue if we are to find a path into the future and hope to be alive as a cultural force in generations to come. Future generations run the risk of further weakening under present conditions. We are indeed an endangered species, not forward, onward, upward as our reluctant father intended, but faltering by the way-side out of view and struggling to be heard and shared our rightful share of economic necessity.

We are still tied to the central government by limited purse strings as we were in the colonial era. Really not much has changed. Budgetary concerns (restraints) are the primary consideration by Central Government and are one of the problems by which we have been held limited and without an outlet for our self-determining goals. The newly formed Local Government groups, a small group of self-motivated limitedly trained officers of our islander people, mark a new self-determination in the Out-Islands. Unlike Nassau, which is now self-determined towards eating up almost 80 percent of National resources and revenue (with good results) we are faltering in the island breeze without a leg to stand on, suffering from a lack of support for our much-needed up rise and the need for the organization of our people. Yet like Maya Angelou, that great African- American literary figure of the modern age we maintain, "We shall rise."

The much-needed total development of these outlying islands will be a total asset to our country as a whole. The effect will be to relieve our crowded city centers and provide an alternative for crime-wary, congested city dwellers who migrated to these crowded city centers from the relative freedom of these islands in the first instance. How a little island, Nassau, the smallest in our archipelago can be the only one relied upon to warehouse our burgeoning national resources shows some lack of foresight. This approach is quite limited as the near future will force these resources to be relocated elsewhere, why not begin to develop those areas of future-need now?

The overcrowding of the little island of Nassau was unnecessary and has provided a rather limited access of the totality of the Bahamian people to much-needed educational and professional development resources. We have been appeased for generations by crafty politicians who provide us at times of national decision with only the necessity items like utilities and safe roadways. Our educational resources are limited to secondary school, with the occasional offering of professional education courses by concerned private institutions centered elsewhere off of the island. We have had an unfortunate history, which ironically ended in our ownership of the most exotic, tropical landscape; in that we are most fortunate. It cannot end there. We must continue to develop the total land mass and further develop the minds of Islander people with the resource needed to sustain ourselves here in these out islands for the coming centuries. World resources will become increasingly more limited and competitive; we must act now before these islands fall further back into the tyranny we are presently in.

While the world sees through the media the glamour of the island of Nassau and Paradise Island, the new grand development of Freeport and Grand Bahama Island, with its industrial giants, there is another Bahamas untold, undiscovered, The Out Islands. These islands make up 80 percent of the total land mass of the Bahamian Islands yet presently contain only 20 percent of the total national population. Where have all the islanders gone?

Nassau, the industrialized world and Freeport are the answer. Our new national proclamation in Nassau is, "I come from the Islands." The Islands are no longer anything but a mythical destination realized only in times of need for forgetting the woes and stresses of the industrialized world. We wish for the Out Islands to be always that unique, free destination for the average world traveler. We have a splendid product in our tropical environment and our friendly people, which must not change; to continue in the delivery of gentle, friendly service to traveling, welcome guests is one of our main goals in our economic puzzle.

This Island niceness for which we have come to be known is perhaps our best discovery. It propels us, motivates us and drives up to continue to offer such human qualities to the world. It may become a cliche that we are known to be this way, not so. This niceness is an everyday part of our world, which clears our mind of its mischief and other erroneous potential disasters. In this niceness we remain innocent and free from the harshness seen in other shared parts of the world. We need only to take the much-needed suggested measures to secure a planned, matured approach to society building both for ourselves and for future generations of Bahamians and world travelers alike.

We are inextricably linked. The resource of people building whether here in the Out-Islands or in the industrialized world benefits us all. Sooner or later through some God-controlled process our paths will cross, in the Out-Island getaways or in the city centers around the industrialized world. Your betterment serves you well in that instance and our betterment serves us in the manner we are able to exchange. What is at stake is not only a matter for we Islanders to consider but the necessity by us all of healing our world locations and making our world a better place. Ours, Eleuthera and the other Out Islands of the Bahamas, are foreseeable immediate needs.

In the Blessed Moments of Morning

In the blessed moments of morning
Before the creepy moments of sunlight's magic
You awake to find your head is clear
The distanced traveled the night before unknown

Awakened refreshed and full of zest for another day's light
Anytime you feel this way is the beginning of a new delightful day.
Beating the sun to rise is a wonderful feeling in the morning.
This gives you the illusion that extras in determination are yours.

I shuttled to the shower, near wobbly, filled with excitement that I had beaten the sun.
Cleared the chores of the morning and gathered those brackets necessary for mercantile adventures of the day.
Jostling across the courtyard with a head of black current sugar plums,
In relative darkness so as not to be discovered the morning by the crowds.
Early morning risers get the trick of life.
It's wonderfully quiet in the morning.

Shuttling past the iron gates of vice and clasp into eerie darkness just beyond the stairs, Near slipped in excitement in knowing I would soon be home.

The delightful feeling, just turning the latch key door seemed invigorating.

Just knowing the magic of another day's treasure is planted out and ready for production, Beating the sun is additional bonus for this.

This morning I met her again, just after the turning of the latch key door.

I did not see her face of smell her perfume; she sent me a note with little musings and matters of interest,

Rekindling our hearts passion, almost making the promise that I might see her again on our shores.

Her divine light eyes, just the softness of her golden hair beat with my breath, I saw the yellow eyes pushing through without fear,

Recommending me to look and find the beauty I had known in the past.

That tiger, that yellow temptress never on the edge but with a glaring biting clasp,

That delightful sweetness of the mouth juicy and with waters of candy dice, near magnets Pulling the earth up to sweetness, rubbing the tummy seems an answer

To ages of weariness, gently soft to clasp, imagine and share delightful moments

On the many shores, white glistening sands, treasures for children and lonely strangers,

If only with our humorous demeanor may make this journey again.

I cannot release the effort but trying for the prize seems a midnight affair one cannot risk.

Seeing the Boganskia, magical, tall, light like Indian chemistry, humorous, sweet, near teary, innocent as the world away, sharing bungalows with lonely empty air, knowing full well that to return to my island would be the treasure life had intended.

How far to go without a caress, is the answer to the strength of this strong-pulling tide lingering on the inside stuck and sometime rising when Boganskia makes her appearance and drives wild the passions brought on by the night.

We may hope to see Boganskia again, with clear pubescent lips, light yellow eyes, the jolly will of a child wrapped up in the clear outline of a profile, a memory of close perfection which seeming not to care, may be the best notion one could ever have of Boganskia's pure magic.
Boganskia's release is my dream.

And so to remember Boganskia on cool light mornings after having beat the sun in the warming is like nirvana itself for a brief moment, this child so sweet and innocent wrapped in the experience of thirty something years, golden weave streaming in the noon days sun, memories of sweet strangers inviting, some protection from this life of loss.
A constant reminder that life's glory is in maintaining these relationships bearing no cost or consequence.

Sweet Boganskia live in my mind forever and see me as the light that envies you, one who needs to know the touch of something more than the ordinary mask.

Sweet Boganskia, sweet disguise if this is not love for any other reason than to claim the life needed to be in tune with nature's call; this could not be you.

And so as magic's tearing ends, Boganskia still deep within the mind, the sun peeks over the horizon.
Pinkish glare preceeding, like no other morning.
Open skies now, time is drifting away beyond the darkness,
Humans starting to rise and shuttle to untold destinations.
Light's magic in the east sees the order of the day.
I do not know what today will bring but I have tasted, sampled the sweetness in a rise with Boganskia's imaginary dream.
She'll come in spring time with some more eerie, sultry delights,
I'll be her servant, fulfill her wishes, do all that I can to maintain her fair.

We may never change, we may never grow
But the memories of Boganskia live on in the mind,
Just remembering is sweet, that fair kiss, those sweet gentle nudgings,
Candid delightful aroma, slight touch of the breast in this I am keeping, maybe early spring.

While the sun still rises, hens crow in the distance,
The enviable golden bloom rising to the world sets a fire to the spirit.
Night-time is over, the coming of a new day at hand

And we made it in, prepared for breakfast and sat down.

Open with the minds of masters burdened with bones and treasures.

Sticks beating as if in the wind, gentle wavers glaring in light surprise

And knowing that night may fall again on the long horizon of a hot summer's day

Is enough to know the cycle may end with days of delightfulness

Is enough to know that being without the vices and needs you know

May be the answer to divinity,

Never cross water with fire, never play envy with shame,

Keeping life crisp and crafty demands the magic of early mornings risings,

Pure organizations need be risked if knowing, master's guise with envious delight Shifting in the back images of the mind.

Travel in some mornings, bring me Boganskia too

So that I might know I've lived in beautiful bounty, nuggets still memorable,

Nothing tainted, just remember the golden sunlight of the early mornings rising

And know that breath and life are one and the same, gasp up to life delights

And see miracles in the middle of the morning.

Sweet Boganskia, how can I forget your delightful, timid smile amidst the permanent, emblem of your face,

Within you there's a miracle waiting to happen, I
would like to be the owner of that prize, Love is not
enough, just a beginning, light eyes
Remembered even through tragedy in the world,
Boganskia gives memories to many lucky enough to
see.

Give us a chance to see this world again.
Keep the will on early morning's risings, powers
shifting
From relative darkness and shadows to wiry
possibilities.
Soon the sky will be tingling, golden, yellow streams
of magic in an empty light blue sky.
Darkness of the morning, Boganskia, sticks beating in
the background, weariness of strangers, you have made
my day.

We'll meet again in the magic of the morning when
tasteful delights like Boganskia's refreshing glares
share with us.
Sweet distance transcending, knowing that this might
be tomorrow, never worry, bring us this magical prize
again.

Softly hurt internal. Needing no fury, just memories,
will be this way again, golden moments…

Why not share?

Scenes of a Daily Fish Market

Bubbling souls, calamity is near.
At the fish market everyone awaits release.
Awaiting expression is nearly a pleasure, blending a treasure, a delight.
Why wait on the world?

Measure yourself by many.
Call me a friend.
In the darkness I am there.
I know your world, a lasting entity, joyous and free.

Enough miracles for all.
Love for the world is divine.
'Tis never ending love need not end.
The warmth in simplicity is generous, no smiles just sincerity.

Prove yourself this love and see the gowns of the evening.
Drawback and see our waiting on these.
Go out and see the world.
Meet the world amid the glaring rays of summer days at the fish market.

A union, a joyous undefined, even calamity is a movement.
Organized chaos.
A village transpired in the act of survival.
See the need for sunlight, brevity, paced, never alone in itself.

The magical prize even on cold winter nights when minds are free.
Nehemiah knows his songs and mastery of great delight.
Control the masses with candy pleasure.
A rock star knows where magic lies in music.

A summer day in the village,
Trophy fishermen know the glory of sunshine's light rays.
They also know the mystery of fish.
Be a part of the world.

There's richness galore in this.
The power of people undefined.
Not in calamity.
Midnight prizes await
As it does memory awaits a happy people.

See fish jump in the village trough.
Live fish sacrificed for all, enjoy this day,
The giver knows magic in hearts divine.
Serene aloft set adrift on a magical aqua glaze.

Summer's days end when village people share their delights.
Sup up and off to bed with tomorrow's shantytown afloat and fine,
The wonderful gestation knows the hearts of many.
Paz Fuera, souls afloat on the sea of life in a village fish market,
Tremendous anew with miracle prizes jumping on wooden rickety plateaus

Cut to perfection tailored for taste,
Free, delightful and willing to serve...

George Major

Everything is Poetry, They Say

Look out on a summer's day when white caps drift aloft on the waters edge, crispy white caps separate the water's edge from the blanket deep of the Atlantic Ocean.

The green, aqua, glistening iridescence transpired through a series of magical light waves toward the shallow depths, brownish creek limestone jutting out in the distance, pronouncing a hiding place for the groups of delicious fair the palette knows so well.

Every thing is poetry they say.

Look at the hummingbird, shivering, dancing, staying aloft for hours at a time,
120,000 beats per minute from the breast as the work of gathering sweet nectar from the rose bush, its daily task, begins over and over again.
The poetry of the hummingbird is not its size but the tenacity with which it hovers for hours awaiting inspection and approval by some human eye, some sort of human touch, validation.
The hummingbird knows the uniqueness of its existence and shares this special time with the few who may come to know miracles and something more in a lifetime of the faithful.
Have you seen hummingbirds on a summer's day?

Then go now to flowers, the hues are just as magical as any other subject known to man.

The canopy, canvas from which these ornaments are selected, is an endless variety as magical and diverse as the human population.

There's something in this mess someone has not said.

See the flowers and know the miracle of life, for within the flower's immaculate conception lies the mystery which rules the world with delight.

The power to balance the largest crystal ball glistening on both ends by congenial, comic mastery, the flower palette never ends, like the miracle of life.

Let's see the hues.

Primarily there's red, the shepherd that leads the eyes in a season.

Along the highway there's red in a season.

I've seen the bright red glare of summer red in June.

The poinsettia tells us so.

The pluming red secular vision of red in a hibiscus is another telling point, different than the gigantic shape of the poinsettia.

The red of the hibiscus is another timid mass, shapely and succulent, a magical makeup of color, fancy and imagination enough to decorate for kings and queens.

Have you ever seen anyone refuse the sight or scent of a flower?

I don't think so.

Nearing the massive red in flowers again comes pink.

Pink is like a cooling miracle, a birth effect, cooling down the spirit allowing for something more to approach.

Is there nectar in pink flowers?

Pinkness in flowers shows serenity, a trust, a mistrust, a common imagination, tipped over the green lawn this display preserved by the most caring of hands.

Pink hibiscus, pink bougainvillea, pink hyperbole.
All examples of the powers of the pink to move the imagination from idle into motion with the active world.
Just pink alone can do it.
Pink is a magical canvas on which to place one's heart and invite the world in for inspection.
A pink heart is a jealous atmosphere, no one can tell how and why.
Try pink and know the difference.
The pink, centuries-old, spinning, glistening weave of the conch shell is another troubling matter.
Though not a flower it has the elegance, the polished appearance to trap the imagination of the world for hours, perhaps years.
Holding in transition memories and wonders never ceasing, shocking pink, deep pink on the locket of a conch shell is the most fantastic experience ever to behold.
Group conch's pink, deep and light among the most explosive miracles known to capture the heart in favor of creation.
Spun from centuries of waiting the conch delivers softness, a pearly pattern to the world like no other imaginable.
I have never seen such as bright a miracle as bright reddish shocking pink on a shell.

See a conch shell and see a miracle of nature glistening, shining with the desire to draw the heart into love so powerful.

Collectors know the power of the conch, centuries and imagination bring about this tremendous magical appearance.

Ode to the conch.

The softness of white in a night jasmine or in the form of a white hibiscus,

Perhaps the white in a happy cow flower over hanging the winding streets, flowering in bloom by the millions,

Passersby through the season are delighted to see the plumage at the farm when the time of the cow flower is nigh.

Painters, many have caught the magic contained in the cool white glow of the cow flower, sometimes seasonally changing to pink.

The cow flower's weave is a magical candescence like no other in the world.

Like a symphony it showers the believer with shivers and night time jazz enough to realize that someone is waiting at the gates,

The pearly gates of heaven for those who approach the delicate balance of nature.

The nighttime wafting and the surprise of night jasmine bring such a delight, such a magical enterprise drifting in the summer sky like no other.

Frankincense and Myrrh probably have something in common with night jasmine. Uncommon and worldly night jasmine is adrift in all the neighborhoods of the

world. Only special villagers get to sample occasionally the magic contained in night jasmine's reward.
Hit the pay-dirt and sniff up on the wafting nighttime air of night jasmine,
Only at night this magical enterprise happens.
Wafting on the horizon of time the soft night jasmine drifts in unsuspecting, taken aloft back to the history of exotic fervor.
Put night jasmine in a bottle, cap it with special figures and know a delight never known throughout the world.
No one can match the beauty of night jasmine wafting aloft from pimpled sweet white flowers.

Let's take the whiteness of the guava lily, numerous and seasonal.
Look at what it delivers, the pinkest passion imaginable.
Biting in to bright sweet pinkish flesh of a seasoned guava produced from the remains of a white guava bloom is an experience unparallel in nature, unique in its own way.
Guavas are special.
Even a hint of white blossoms on a grooming green guava tree sends shivers down the spine.
Place the tree in the heart of some one special and there you have a double miracle, Guavas with special people, I've known a few.
Some magical enterprise convenes over these delights.
I've seen guava gardens burdened down by the will of the creator,
Shucked in bottom landfill with hog-wash and other gruesome materials,

Along with the temptation to walk by and sniff the white jasmine, this enterprise is special.

Only kings and queens need see the magic of white blossoms in spring,

Night jasmine wafting in the summer sky and the pinkish delight

Of gentle guava raging through the mile with iron sweetness that fills the heart with measures of more,

Perhaps next season, we will see.

Some colors carry with them the delight of the ages, the most memorable of these,

Most widely known throughout the world in the magical range of the yellow orange, Varied, figurative and spread far and wide is the beautiful, wiry smacking delight of an orange.

The orange blossoms are white, too numerous to count, too special to behold everyday.

The power contained on one orange blossom is so great as to shock the world.

Anything in contact with an orange blossom knows it ability to pollinate the world.

The mere scent of the whiteness of the orange blossom, a singular delight,

Is a notion which enterprise cannot overcome.

Singular scenting, corporate delights, shivering magical are all contained in one pimpled beautiful white blossom.

Alive for centuries and developing new tastes among the city centers of the world,

The magical white orange blossom knows history, succulent enough for kings,

The coveted treasure of the common man, orange blossoms are divine.

Stand in the middle of an orange grove, in the middle of spring, blossoms in bloom, and you have an experience like no other,

This before the business of the bee, white plumes on green spinners,

Glistened by the magical Protean of the sunlight filtered through the glistening blue air the white plumes of magical white blossoms are fed a daily dose of vitality, connected from the beginning straight to the divine.

Why oranges, nurtured through white blossoms wafting orange medicines for miles out of the grove, scented night time/daytime musks, why this is so magical is no guess but a miracle in waiting, like night jasmine a desired entity so strong that the world can't wait just knowing the products of white blossoms is in itself satisfaction that correctness in nature is such a great reward.

Have you seen or scented the miracle of the whiteness of the orange blossom?

Colors are a mixing affair, a special delight.

Some other anomaly you might have imagined is the cowry like mixture of the rubber vine, a handy presentation of white, lofting puffy white, mixed the the powdery dense whimsy of violet.

Both of these juxtaposed on a single flower, seasonal blooming in the summer sky, deep pockets, containing nectar but no iridescent scent.

Bright enough to pollinate and spread its magic throughout the world the rubber plant is delightful and pleasing to the eyes in appearance like no other you may imagine.

We have rubber plants in the village, non productive though as beautiful in season to happen by, the textured feel of the rubber vines flower like glazed, a pure cool ripping effects the comfort but newly noted once occurred.

The rubber plant though obscure is a delight for the world to happen by.

Masterful in nature colors have the power to effect our imagination, soothing any worry, eliminating any doubt of divine intervention.

Honeybees suckling on a nest of jasmine bush, orange petals, guava lights know the suckling and softness of nature,

There is so much more.

There for example is the succulent bright candy of the cherry tree, white with blossoms in the spring, light nectar pouring with brevity from the spring inside the sap of the cherry tree.

After feeding, cross-pollinating with the bees and moths the cherry green appears to bake in the noonday sun like the white blooming blossom turning eventually into a bright red magic drop of unimaginable zesty delight, the bearing of a tasty prize for the believer in bright red hue.

Like lemon drops so delightful so magical and delightful one cannot resist the appetite for cherries, not to mention cherry pie.

There's poetry in everything they say…

Wander out on a summer morning in the garden and see the varied miracles, sweet blossoms in bloom, candied hued magical delight, varied colors, varied wiry connected avenues to taste.

Add to this the magical existence of Island life, the tranquility of the beaches, the wafting iridescence of the Atlantic, Caribbean Sea and know what existence within God's miracle garden is about.

Imagined centuries ago, within the creator these magical gardens exist today in the world, no mere memories in the mind, skippers on gossamer wings still exist, the odyssey of discovery still exist, the play kill imagination discovery still exists.

The world is a magical place, swept on a island like a drifting coconut searching the entire world for a whom, exist with this delightful miracle, I suggest belief in knowing that miracles are many, happen the on a miracle a day.

Peace love and happiness, through colors as streaming as the rainbow, candied miracle as natural and delightful as the mint sucker in a green tea on a summer porch over looking the green ocean.

Let it rip its way through time, lofty speeding, delightful.

Peace out….Havana shines, knock out Hong Kong and know why.

Luminescence exists God knowing.

Colors are here to stay.

Inquiry and Knowledge

The need and inquiry of knowledge, the query to our superiors to develop further our wonderful democracy for future generations and ourselves, is evident. This freedom we are aware of. We are aware of the great social and economic freedom of our neighbors to the north in America; their continued economic, racial and emigrational struggles over the many generations during which we, our ancestors, were present. We must compare ourselves to that society and ask ourselves the question, "Why have we not similarly, in a parallel manner, developed?"

Some of the problems are obvious; others lurk beneath the surface. Many of the problems we are reluctant to debate on a national stage. Our protectionist measures taken by Central Government are some of the root causes for both our lack of the development of our democracy and the lack or potential chaos in our society. We have been slow and cautious in our approach to development; perhaps in some instances rightly so. Crime is rampant in our city centers so I am reluctant to out rightly blame all of the problems on Government. The minds of many of our people need changing. How do you truly, effectively change the hearts of man?

God has given us the answer for centuries yet many of us lack the resolve and foresight to see the need for fully adapting to the suggestions of our Heavenly Father's advice. This notion has attributed to chaos in the streets of our city centers as many of our people lack the compassion and intensity needed to love their fellowman as instructed by God. I pray for a solution to our reluctance to heed such historically proven religious instruction. The redemption of the heart I feel is the key to Salvation both in Heaven and here in our small country. With this ideal personally taken to heart I go on about my daily task of living and preparing myself not only as an author of literary works but a student in service to God and community, the former first.

There is great potential in our Islands. We must continue on a national level to find ways of encouraging the positive development of our Out Island communities, while maintaining their unique innocence and tranquil environments. Through development we cannot lose these aspects of our communities. The notion of being laid back must be dispelled and replaced with the notion of permanent, positive development through education, socialization and economic development. We must rise nationally above the base needs of infrastructure to the more noble notions of personal development, some attainment of comfort and the notion of propelling our Out Islanders into the future with some security and less doubt about financial concerns.

Many of the problems associated with drugs, crime, and theft are due to insecurity about one's personal economic future. In an attempt to secure themselves financially Islanders, in their isolation, became greedy and were exploited by the Evils of the drug trade. Since the level of policing in the Out Island has increased and the visibility of the Islands is more evident through the national media this activity has largely ceased, evident only through isolated reports on the national news.

We continue, in our relative isolation, to find our rightful place in the modern world.

George Major

The Golden Rays of Sunshine

When the golden rays of sunshine come guarantee the
brilliance of the day,
Invite me into the world.
The world so starry, types of many looming, lofty
clouds permeate
Without doubt that world is where we are, buried in the
mirth of sensuousness,
A wild way to desire, and knowing now of that
darkness that will come,
Taking away the gleaming paradise of the day.

Invite me into a world where lovers play a zesty game
called hope,
Enlightened, amused and filled with the sugar coatings
temptation knows so well.
While during the day the wicked trickster shuttles out
his tricks in merry delight,
The madness over, the cool rays of the sun has brought
the patient happiness
Into the days amid joyous heads, laughter failing to
rear its ugly head.
Just warmth, just paradise, enough for the day when
hope is near
For the many weary of the night before the certainty of
sunshine.
Let go the night bring the sunshine in the murky waters
of hope say.

So muddled we are, these golden rays of sunshine,
The cherishing nature of birds and wildlife,

Luminous grandeur awaits the world on sunlit canopies
Longing for the sweet pleasures awaiting.
Cherish the sunlight mornings, rays of sunlight bring
hope to the weary mind,
The mind needs telling, the sun's golden rays write
down their hope for the day,
So divine and awesome never refused, never
unwanted;
No one hates the miracle of days.

Then in the morning when murky waters know not the
sunlight of the morning memories, Do the task of
remembering the pleasure of a stroll in the sunlit
morning
Beside the glistening aqua maze of the shadowy sea,
The Caribbean side.

Stanzas of delight bring about the notions wishes,
Desires of the heart exposed in all the will of nature
lies the mysteries of the sunlight, Ever seen, ever sure
the wicked of the night cry await in anger,
Their nightmare has just begun.

Ah, the glorious sunlight.
Have I convinced you enough to see the morning's
golden rays,
The magical hearts dancing along the shadowy seaside,
the Caribbean side?
El Caribbean, sunlight lurking, dancing, skipping,
Desires dream travels with the sunlight you know.

The murky waters a haze, out pops the grouper away
from midnight's doom,

And brings home the heat and the madness contained
in the dungeons
Beneath the murky shores.
Further out the iridescent miracles awake with sheer
delight
As if a moment not cherished in the world has just
begun.
The distaste of night seeming, slowly awakening,
The golden sunshine coupled with rays of dark doom
The domain of the gentle, the wicked, hiding the rays
and skipping,
Skimming the surface.

See the gossamer wings skip across the waters,
Awakened only with the day a fantasy unrequited
And maddened the envy of all,
The sunlight's magic rays revere the sky,
Iridescent dreams waft, sugar plum delights,
Early in the morning arise with brevity
And memories not weary of the night's known
madness,
The golden rays of sunlight bring hope to the world.

In a villager's head nothing more than another miracle
defined
Wanting nature to arise not cherished by the cherubim
magic
Whisked away before the spectacle ends,
Work out today's measures of weary bread and feed
the masses teacakes,
Morning coffee knows the warmth of golden rays.

A warm heart knows the warmth of golden rays,

Drifters cool, relaxed with unknown treasures of a
world of fantasy
Make their way in preparation for the upcoming
glorious delight,
The warm rays hit the heart a streaking blow
Through which enters the murky villager's laughter,
Silent composed never filled with unknown intentions,
Listen to the golden rays of the sun, make me home
this place
Among the certain magic of the divine absorption of
sunlight's rays.

Feed the masses today, says the sun's bright rays,
Gather with them the hope of iridescent miracles,
A never-ending stream of contentment, who sends us
where,
Who knows our hearts feed us with the miracle of age,
These villagers know the miracle of paradise.

Village life coupled with the miraculous rays of
sunshine
On the glorious morning rise, levitating high in the sky
And trembling with the certainty that this might be the
day never-ending,
A miracle heart appears among the verves, these
miracles,
These rays of sunshine we never know how and why
they appear
Yet they delight us every day in the history of the
world,
This the history, the memory of the suns rays skipping
across the canopy
With the magic of a sunlit world in itself a delight,

George Major

The sunlight asks, "How far shall I rise?"

Wafting sugar crisps know the head's desire,
Know the world's desire for sunlit mornings,
Looming sugar puffed clouds, sinking iridescent blue
hues in the background
Know the warmth of the sunlight, the magic of these
know the way of winding, unraveling throughout the
canopy of the sky.

Believe it or not each ray of sunlight carries with it a
miracle,
A glowing enterprise, a certainty discovered anywhere
on the world.
Sun rays are powerful, catch a sun ray's delight
Like the rainbow butterfly aloft in the meadow haze of
morning,
Bright blue, circled black, reds aglow, the powerful
lofty gleam of wings
Held aloft wafting on magic looms, warm currents
adrift
With care and magical notions of the sun's rays
On bright sunlight mornings in summer,
Winter now passed see the miracle,
See the sunshine's bright gleaming tease on rising
notions
Minds awaken bringing out aloft the sunlight,

This magic sequence shares the iridescence of the
world away.
The magical sunlight may last forever, the warm
butterflies know,
Collecting their nectars, sniffing out perfumes,

Night jasmine disguised in lemon delights,
Sugar fill nectars for the looming magical creatures
Even butterflies know miracles.

And when the sun hides, covers its warm, energetic
sunrays,
The cool of winter approaches even on summer days
Opened with the warm rays of glorious sunshine.
White light gleams with sunshine,
The divine controller knows the needs of the world,
Have you ever seen a white butterfly?

Summer days, ever-shifting, glorious, wafting
energetic rays
Filled with the magic of a warmth golden in
appearance,
Even summer days know the warmth of the world.
A glorious change, a magical disappearance,
A joyous exchange of contentment, miracles, madness,
Contentment all on a summer's day,
Warm hearts know the world on a calming, long,
delightful summer day.

Come into the world with a need to know the delight,
Lord Jesus bring me into the world, our hearts known
in your grace,
These mornings when golden rays of miracles open
our minds
To the miracles of nature arise us with delight.
Know our hearts, our desire for a golden world of
miracles never ceasing,
This is the way of the world, nearly magical,

Just warm with hope of future summer, wafting warm,
days to come.

Add with this the miracle of seashores,
Lofty beaches a way so wide out of this world, aqua,
light, promise cool desire,
Long stretches of puffed white delight, sinking brevity
depths, miracles,
Beaches in a world filled with golden rays of sunshine
in the morning,
Given to us all we have a way in this world
To share the delight of these gifts.

Lord Jesus grant us this need to see this world on
magical sunlit mornings.

A Week in the Life of an Island Man

Recently I had the opportunity to spend a wonderful day at Northside Beach Club in Rock Sound, Eleuthera, Bahamas. A group of friends and I, including six beautiful girls from the United States, had a lovely day at the beach-side restaurant. The beach itself is one of the most breath-taking in the entire archipelago of islands, and the food and service at the restaurant-bar proved to be wonderful. We ended up making plans for the beach party after spending a memorable night of partying and dancing at the Fish Fry at Governor's Harbor the night before.

The fish fry is a weekly event that takes place in Governor's Harbor at Anchor Bay. It's mostly a community street party, a superb display of food, drinks, dancing and great music played by the islands most famous DJ, Chaffi. The Fish Fry takes place every Friday night from 7PM until Midnight, when all the locals from all over the island congregate for a street-dancing festival.

The setting is a roadside thatch venue at Anchor Bay and there are eight thatch stalls set up to serve you many of the Bahamas' most popular dishes including: fried fish, conch salad, cracked conch, stewed fish, barbecued chicken, grilled conch and many more varieties of simply marvelous dishes including peas and rice and lobster salad to name a few. In attendance you'll also find a variety of Club Med guests and G.O.'s from the all-inclusive beach resort located just across the island on the ocean side of Governor's

179

Harbor, as well as tourists living in the many vacation cottages scattered in every village along the island.

After our wonderful night at the Fish Fry we headed over to Ronnie's Rebel Room, located a short walk away on the famous island across the bridge, Cupid's Cay, where we spent the night dancing away to reggae, rap and calypso music again orchestrated by the delightful Chaffi. We partied until 3AM in the morning and had a wonderfully fun road trip forty miles up the island back home to our village of Tarpum Bay.

The girls, mostly from Chicago and St. Louis, consider Tarpum Bay their home as well since they come down to visit and have fun with us twice a year during the month of May and December. Two things are happening during both of those times, the *mahi mahi* (dolphin fish) are running on the western Atlantic just east of the island, and during the Christmas season we have a wonderful nation-wide celebration called *Junkanoo*.

Junkanoo dates back to the early slavery days, started by the slaves as a way of releasing their frustrations against their masters in a non-violent way. The *rushes*, as the songs are called, are done musically with the aid of goat-skin drums, cow-bells and whistles, similar to carnivals in Rio.

Any Friday night is a great time to have a party here, enjoying the handiwork of the natives and the effects of the wonderful pineapple and coconut rum, not to mention the Bahama Mamas, a wonderful fruity drink concocted by some Nassauvian mixologist.

So there we were on Saturday midday at the North Side beach bar being hosted by manager Julian and his wonderful chef in the kitchen, Miriam. We spent most of the day tanning on the beautiful North Side beach, which borders the western Atlantic Ocean, and taking the necessary cooling swim to break the beating rays of the noon-day sun.

The girls love this beach and visit it religiously each time they come down to bring back memories of frolicking in the warm Bahamian hospitality and sunshine. We really love to see them break away during these times they visit us, leaving behind the baggage of U.S. taxes, jobs and family, delightfully caressing each other with lavish servings of love and friendship.

Eleuthera is generally famous for its unique charm and its ability to keep dedicated tourists coming back again and again because of its relaxed, charming people and its lovely natural pink sandy beaches. You don't have to go far to experience any of this fun since there are so many beaches and people waiting to take you on a tour of the island they are so proud to be a part of. The people are delightful and always willing to share some of themselves with their tourists in order to give them the greatest travel experience they have ever had.

If you're interested in having the time of your life come down to Eleuthera, Bahamas, and experience the culture of an island filled with tranquility, love and lasting friendship.

George Major

Tourist Beauty

I am about to describe a travel situation that is not for everyone; but for those who love finding a second home in a travel experience, it is ideal.

I live in beautiful Tarpum Bay, Eleuthera, Bahamas. Tarpum Bay is a tropical, friendly waterfront Out-Island community in the Bahamian islands. We are somewhat remote but accessible by a few major airlines originating out of Miami and other U.S. cities, especially the flag carrier of the Bahamas, Bahamasair.

We are located 120 miles east of Miami and 60 miles east of Nassau. We have regular mail-boat service weekly, which many people are choosing more and more because of its low cost and unique charm. We are frequented by passing sailboats and yachts; curious people traveling and looking for picturesque ports and charming villages in which they can come aboard and relax on, among the friendly natives and the local flavor and cuisine.

Tarpum Bay is beautiful. It's a splendid place for any globe-trotting tourist looking for friends and a pleasant place to call home. Over the past twenty years we have become the second home of many return travelers who make their pilgrimage to our shores annually. We have been delighted with this happening and have quietly become the favorite place for several families who have enjoyed our unique people and the friendliness and acceptance of our island lifestyle.

The village is a waterfront community with its beautiful bay stretching for miles and miles as the island curves in the far distance, creating a lovely body of water that is just a most tremendous sight to be viewed by cityscape-weary travelers. Tourists exclaim at every opportunity of how they love Tarpum Bay because of its lovely waterfront harbor and its friendly people.

We are still untouched by much of the tourist development that goes on in the country's major cities like Nassau and Freeport. The town is made up of a collection of quaint beautifully-painted. neat houses, especially along the waterfront. The splash of pastel colors adorning the many buildings, many of them ancient, is captivating. The freshness of the turquoise waters bordering the seawall as one makes his way along the waterfront highway is simply astounding. This scenery is the single most captivating landmark that Tarpum Bay has.

Locals as well as visitors congregate day and night along the waterfront shore, where each evening the daily cleaning and selling of the day's fish catch is carried out by the individual fishermen located in several different locations along the waterfront harbor. This is truly a spectacular sight as visitors and tourist clamor around the fishermen, bargaining and teasing for the best prices on lobster, conch, grouper and other popular varieties of great tasting fresh fish for the evening meal.

Conch are stored in wired water gardens just out beyond the swimming areas where the locals can be seen enjoying the splendor of the summer surf in order to combat the warm summer days. All of this is played out before an unsuspecting audience of travelers who traverse the waterfront looking for that special scenery or some unique island memory to take back home from their travel experience.

They do get those opportunities in Tarpum Bay. Our treasured visitors come to us from various places around the world. What is unique to us and something to treasure, is that they have formed the habit of adopting some family and friends who treasure them and hang out with them during their travels along the island and on into the ocean on daily fishing trips. These adopted friends and families feel a certain pride in keeping the friendships with their new travelers goings and do as much as they can to foster the new friendships, which end up in some rather unique exchanges of visits and counter-visits to the cities from which the tourists descend.

Our local people have learned to cultivate these relationships greatly and are now moving into the next phase of encouraging these visitors to stay in our local community. As a result of the outpouring of love and friendships fostered by these annual travelers, new homes are being built by several tourists who have vowed to make this lovely tropical paradise their home. Tarpum Bay has certainly benefited from these relationships that have grown out of the simplicity of world travel and a curiosity to get to know more than just the physical location to which these tourists travel. They all share the unique quality of wanting to get to know and love the people who inhabit these islands to which they travel.

Perhaps this is a new trend in tourism and traveling which has turned out to be quite an asset to both these tourists and the local recipients. These newly forged friendships generate some truly interesting exchanges between the visitors and their adopted families who do all they can to accommodate the needs of their guests. In one instance, one of the tourists paid for his vacation by purchasing and delivering a used car for export to the island from his area in St. Louis. This not only paid for his vacation while on the island that year but paid for his transportation as well. Now he has a car that he can request to use whenever he is on the island for his vacation time. Others bring boats down for their use when they travel during the fishing season. They employ the help of the local fishermen who are more than eager to make a new friend and assist these visitors in having a great travel experience. Most of the families here have guest cottages and villas for rent to our beloved visitors.

One of the largest activities enjoyed by our new friends is fishing. These gentlemen, mostly from Chicago and St. Louis, organize annual fishing tournaments which they attend twice a year during the fishing season for *mahi-mahi*, barracuda, and dolphin (not the "Flipper" variety). They have a tremendous time during the winter season in their adopted home villas fraternizing and generally having a great time enjoying the local people and the local Bahamian beer which they have come to love.

I look forward to their annual arrival mostly during the Christmas season, when our annual *Junkanoo* celebration is at its peak. During other times of the year the wives of these men and some of their single friends travel down separately from the men to have their own space. They enjoy sunning on the lovely beaches, and getting out each night to a local bar for the festive late night dancing and fraternizing by the local people. We just love it.

There's no telling where this brand of mutual loving exchange will go. It's fantastic to see our visitors among us enjoying themselves as if they were at home. They dance, laugh, enjoy the music and engage us in conversation as we move around the club, looking for something exciting to do. Our wonderful friends provide us with the excitement of new friends and acquaintances, all with loving ways and pretty faces to enjoy.

It's fun to see a newly divorced woman come down and mix with us perhaps in her attempts to forget her misery at home by getting out on the dance floor and tapping out some newly learnt Bahamian Calypso dance. Our job is to entertain and ensure them a pleasant, friendly good time.

We hope that each time we encounter a new visitor we fill them with the desire to return and visit with us again. We've greatly benefited from tourism and love to promote our island and our village as the premiere place to spend a small portion of your lifetime among friends that will love you for who you are.

This unique experience is available for those tourists looking for a special experience in their traveling.

The Old Trickster

The old trickster shifted his position and juxtaposed his
intentions on passers by.
The lemon look in his eye was descriptive and telling.
There were things on his mind.
Was he telling them?
The trickster eyes as best he could the objects that
appeared before, cocksta cocked,
The eyes positioning them was the problem.
He tried as best he could the see those gleaming
images that made his heart happy, Throwing out of
balance those reminiscent hauntings of his day;
Sometimes he managed a smile crooked and disguised,
the trickster at his art;
What had he imagined?

There were memories of nighttime, shadows, crickets
chirping,
Eerie images brought by long distances between his
bereavement;
He had not had his day.
The trickster, glamorously disguised, interrupted
reason
With his imitation genuine humor; he knew how to
awaken the imagination,
Sending his many tyrants in pursuit of his vanity;
The trickster barely alive but hanging by the hinge
With a vivid imagination and taste for life;
He wanted to be here.

The surrounding trinkets he carried were his wealth,

The reason for his prolonged existence;
Secretly he ruffled these in his pockets and tickled himself
That skimmy smile dripping off El Rostra Lagusto El Caribbean Panacea.
Would his trinkets pay the passage to nirvana?
Pocketed like a stylish vagabond, shifting, cockled, straining,
The trickster needed a way out.

Now trickery is an art, he knew that, he perfected his craft with his life;
His incessant hubris was well known,
Hear him snicker as through the ages he breaks his interlude with brackish speed,
Hehe; the old trickster was sure he would win, he would have his way,
His trinkets knew, rumbling his pockets impishly and otherwise.

On long summer days when hearts are fleeting up ·to the sky,
The surface of the water shimmering alone hiding from the sun
Shaded by the eyes of passers by, taken in for refreshment
And jaded with the glimmer of hope given to the selective minds of many.
The trickster knew this secret; he kept this transfixed in his imagination,
From this he did not, would not drift far.

Infinitely he returned in hopes of jubilation; he had
found his place.
The trickster reminiscent of his past, cockled,
transfixed,
Lifted himself into the light of day, el Rostra
shimmering in the wind
Never knowing how his day might end; knowing his
desire for the night;
He had nothing else left to survey, he had seen the sea
And knew the sweetness of discovery; he had had his
day.

Now shifting, wobbly, limp and filled with trinkets,
He made his way to the secret place to see the Panacea
Lifting himself suspended in time indefinite
quenchment
Knowing now he could go home.
How would home be, better than this?
This is his secret place.

The old trickster, shifting, wobbly, impish at times,
cockled,
Straining in the glare of the noon day sun, reminiscent
of his secret place,
El rostra hiding his eclectic nightmare resided in his
secret place;
Would not go home as if he had nothing to live for,
That impish smile hiding trinkets.
The trickster made his way to his secret place,
The panacea glittering above the shifting glaze taken in
and cooled,
Hiding from the strength of the sun.

Summer mornings are telling, beneath the glazing another day begins
Not revealing its intentions unlike the darkness of night;
Deceptive they bring with them the hopes of gleaming window swept idea-logs. Especially consecutively summer mornings are the answer
To the burnings and goings on unexplained without true intention;
The trickster knew these summer mornings.

For more than a century gathering trinkets, stealing really,
His interlude brushed by bright delightful el rostras.
His trinkets taken in, cockled, impish,
He made his way about the world on summer mornings.

Tray in hand, dashing, cockled, impish his hand had servings, many servings,
Bringing refreshments and cockled smiles
Delivering cockled trinkets to strangers (frenzied, colorful, delightful strangers).
Still wobbly, the shifting character made his way along corridors trickery,
Impish, smiling, his disguise hiding trinkets,
Hiding the very purpose of his imagination, sheer trickery.

At times the trickster, with impish gaze, cockled, straining, gave up trinkets.
The gathered in his secret place knew the good of tricks,

The trickster played along, wobbly, shifting, cockled,
impish smile,
The gathered in his secret place taking in
The glittering rays of summer skipping from the
panasea
Atop the shifting glaze of flat aqua layers, the trickster
took his place.
Balanced atop a shaky, ancient rift in a cockled gaze,
transfixed
The trickster delivers trinkets to the gathering drifters
in.
Disguised beneath a crooked smile the delightful
trickster probes,
Without confrontation he delivers trinkets, pockets
bulging on the inside,
Impish and unexplained his trinkets remain.

So now on summer days long into the centuries ahead,
Cockled, impish, tricky, the trickster with his delight
Resides affront the panasea, sea rays skipping,
Sun's rays glittering atop the shimmering aqua mass
Taken into pockets for refreshment.
The trickster sits atop an ancient, rickety rickster
remembering trinkets,
Delivering trinkets to the gathered
Occasionally sipping the sweet orange rum el rostro
Shining with glee, the old trickster made it home, his
trinkets shining,
Safe forever in his imagination, beaming,
Sharing with the masses, cockled, impish, tricky
The trickster made his pay and moves on delightful,
cool,
Disguised on summer days delivering trinkets.

George Major

Old, shifting trickster.

Sweet nature's answers to the tyranny of village life

It was 6:05 PM.

The shadows of the evening began to fall.

One could see that dusk was coming; yet the skies were opened up with a gleam as never had been seen before…

The sight of the western sky shimmered with excitement

As it opened itself up for the viewing of the few souls who had never seen its sake before.

Now dusk time is a magic time in a village, a time when weary villagers

With heads full of the tasks of the day before still need refreshment,

Before the nighttime sky.

So we gather in the evenings around a makeshift vendor

Breathing, worried, knowing nothing of the coming day ahead,

Yet desiring an experience so full and free as we have never seen before,

For village life demands it so.

Days are hard, arduous, long and filled with drudgerous tasks and labor-filled moments So tiring that any infant would fall knowing the future ahead in a village.

Life in a village innocent yet filled with rifts and shadows,

The likes of which were never known to the unfamiliar.
Life in a village leaves one hungry for scenery; depravity of the soul
Is an illusion sought out by passers-by in villages so vague and drifting,
Lacking structures, defining the skyline so familiar to the mind.

Scanty, sometimes filthy villages leave the wonderer with a scanty view of life.
From this view emerges a need for the glory of creation;
Summer spent nights drifting by the seashore in search of that same familiar scenery,
Like washing rags with dirty water, expecting brightness out of rags,
Like life in a village so undefined.

Any hint of creation is welcomed in a village;
Even the occasional glimpse of the nighttime angels hovering in straight lines
Hanging high above the sky,
Providing the needed refreshment of the villager's needy life.
Look up at the sky and see this mystery revealed; all villagers know.

Coolness, glittering sunshine, scattered seas, nighttime skies
And sometimes the newness of the evening sun as it nestles

Between the horizon and the imagined exterior wall of
the universe;
The newness of the sunset racing precisely due to
speed,
According to time immortal.

Evening suns are like the hanging barriers protruding
empty,
Filling fictitious imagination with enlightened visions
and goodness
For the soul to soak up the sea of illusion.
Evening sun in a village is an occurrence
So creative and magical for the first-time viewer;
Its newness a memory forever imprinted on the mind,
A memory forever remembered and recollected, not
imagined
And brought about by inquiry, ill-natured,
introspective view.

Don't give up on life in a village.

Though narrow, sometimes confining, the route of
escape is open.
The many discoveries to be made in a village
Are boundless beyond the imagination found only by
the lives,
Applied for the centuries of time when life in a village
Grew from a blade of grass and surpassed the
skyscrapers
Jetting beyond the glitter of glass-filled buildings and
ended
Becoming a stream of lively, fascinating, sometimes
bewildering experience

Like never before imagined in the world.

Teeming with nature and shadows propped up like the setting of the evening sun
The village life surpasses, through its unhindered progression
Into the unforeseen future,
It surpasses any other stream of life as we know it or known to man.
The glories on a morning when surprising to the wake
Of shining shadows in streams like spiraled angels
Making their way from heaven,
Descending with bundles of light and flowering sweetness,
Night jasmine a clue to the mystery suspended in the night time air of a village,
Teeming with nature defined only by inhabitants so lively,
Protruding as if in a mirror, dangling against the horizon like the sun,
Endless in the western sky on an evening when wandering out
To make his peace with the world the villager stumbles
On a scenery so vast in magnitude
His mind had opened up to take the fantastic spectacle in view,
When heaven falls out in response to the need of the villager
To make his comfortable mind see the vision
Which heaven needs to create in his imagination,
Making his view of the world through village life a spectacle

To behold by the masters who for centuries have claimed, in hiding,
That the village lacked ingenuity and imagination.

Hidden from the view of public eye they made this claim,
Although seeing heaven through the view like the villager sees
The looming magic of the western sky filled with polish glitter,
Gold in abundance hidden from view in sheer delight that others,
Unknowing might place the villager in another place with the circumspect
View the sunsets in a western sky amidst a village life
Lacks the inspiration needed to propel the imagination of man beyond its greatest depths Returning him to that nirvana which only in his imagination he has seen unknowing Whether he will get there, the setting of the evening sun in the western sky
Is indication enough that the villager will get his promise, his nirvana,
His heaven perhaps looming like the sun, glittering gold,
Streaks unresting, magical, hovering like angels of historic light
Propelling untold stories with this nirvana, this heaven resting on the minds of villagers Throughout the western world, too looming in the sky of the village.

Village life's sweetness comes even in the evening of the sunset.

With the magical delight unending the villager sets out afoot.

Expecting but not receiving, giving but not receiving that magical intended prize,

His nirvana undefined, until that day the villager goes out to see the setting sun

Under the freshness of the evening sky,

Looming golden sun in the light of shadows undefined,

Lives of villagers in the mix of masses teeming to the shores

Seeking the excitement of village life.

Hungry masses needing the refreshment of village life,

Alluring, in contrast, melodious, filled with nature, suspended in animation,

Fulfilling in magical mysterious ways so gentle

Certain among uncertainties in the world unhindered by the passing of time,

Untouched by the moving of many scarred and weary travelers seeking refreshment

As never had by experiences rifting throughout the modern world.

Some have seen nirvana,

Some have seen nirvana in the golden streams of cool sunlight softly shadowing, Disfiguring myth, suppressing all that goes before the nature of the world.

Then comes the heaven, sight unseen but hoped for like nirvana that eternal glory

When peace gives in its hand and leaves the village life and traveler

Defenseless and free of searching freedom resting idly by as time goes on unhindered, Worries free, curiosity killed, illusions drifted away just solid peace remaining,
Fight for freedom ended in the surrendering of the will to imagination.

Then the village life and traveler can rest by the feet of mighty giants too few to mention, Creators of the world, given the ultimate praise of the heart imagined by man.
Sight unseen this heaven exists beyond the skies, frontiers.

Looming upon the rock the villager remembers the sun setting in the western sky,
Gold sandwiched between the end of the earth and the wall of the universe
Racing defined by nature the villager needs no other reminder of divinity in the world.
Village life is sweet on these sweet summer days,
Seeing sunsets drifting below the village world
While passersby seek out delights of the vendor
Dicing God's creation for their sheer delight...

George Major

A Writer Confesses

My life has changed.
I am a believer.
I live with only one notion these days.
To make it here and paint in prose, free-verse
nonetheless.

I make my mood before going down and rise with the
sun.
Unknowing and true sense of purpose.
This notion is grand I know,
I know the magic of the days.

Sun rising in the east pops over gleam,
Rustling waiter in the trees near God's breath,
The ghost of vision imagined in and I am ready for the
world.
Face another day in delight.

Candy visions and notions of needing naked prize.
Touch me there, there in the heart of mind and move
my lover within me.
Deep sensual creativity know me today.
Take from me the notion of knowing more, go deep
and stride with delight atop the masses.

Straighten thy groove and know the magic of sensual
delight.
It's deep this notion drives.
Not topical behaviour.

Touching weaned and never the foolish enterprise it used to be.

Even lovers know the question of when and how.
Just need my love and I am there beside you to guide you through the steps.
This naked writer has in mind an enviable position,
A cleft of magic and fingers posing in vision know the way to nirvana.

Lay back and take it all in.
Under the summer's sky at night, stars in the heavens.
No one around but the soul of a lover met in disguise,
Lay in the lap of luxury, tonight is yours.

You met this lover on a rendezvous stricken out of your notion,
You're here for your lover's prize.
Give him a possession he can remember forever.
Breasts and scents like candles, like the stars up there on summer's nights.
He kisses you beneath your breath, you quivering internally with delight.

The chills running down your spine feel his breath on your skin and peeling back the prize you feel your lover's rock tight within your grasp.
Call him up and lick a vision what a taste of candy on the tongue of time.
Lick it last before it gets away,
Every wet drip before the magic warmness dies beneath your breath.

You will have this lover forever.
You have tasted the magic within and felt the hives
and bumps of his skin, and drank down with delight
the nectar of time immemorial.
This lover knows you and your movements, he feels
you deep within his heart.
He will remember you like the tremors he feels in
waking moments when desire builds his heart.

You know this lover well.
Move with him around the house, summon him up on
cold winter nights when you need to remember him in
your lap.
Staring into your eyes, surrounding your breasts with
circles, lisping sheer breath in night's grasp just out of
lights horizon.
No one can see but imagine you and your lover well in
the notion when hearts beat like sugarplums stumbling
on some light prize.

They saw you go out of the light and knew your lover
was there.
They know the sensuous behaviour, the animal that
you are, roar and on fire.
Sniffing at the tail of hot lovers filled with prize, pretty
in the face and full of potential.
Lovers know and saw you slip into the warm magic of
night just beyond the night lover waiting and
wondering what caress or relief he may get tonight.

Bring your skirt with you, let him peep the magic and
look up your prize, though you cannot hear his refrain

you feel the shifting of his heart as he licks bright heaves of sweat off your skin.

Look out to the waters edge and swallow like a dog in heat as lover wafts sweet breath down your thighs open letting his delightful tongue gaze up gullets.

Hot knives like butter cut through your skin.

Shiver in delight at this.

This night might come no more.

None knows beyond the horizon.

At least you had a night when magic dripped and gullets filled with prized glazes peered out into the naked night and saw her clasping at her skirt.

Vision of naked rides in sight, maybe, keep this night forever in your mind.

We might meet again lover.

We might come to know the fullness of all I possess in white heat with one or two naked thrusts and heaves.

I know your breast so well.

I smell your breath and long for you on long winter evenings.

I know your mind and search you out in crowds.

To see your smile is to know you still care as on that summer night when I knew the passion of you deep with in my palette.

I'll know you yet with warm heaves, one or two delightful throws, one enviable night in a village with no eyes, and minds on others.

I'll know you in the leaves or on the beaches.

We'll come to know the comfort in houses.

We're lovers on the run not together out of shame that some might know why I desire thee.
I know you are my prize, the one to know unseeming with torchlights you come to me teasing, I saw you the other night but could not rise over.

I'll know you well.
Wait for me one evening, flash me in with memory.
Let me know the desires of your heart deep with in you.
I'll give you everything I am that day and live to see you on.

This may go on an on forever when we can.
Night magic unreprised, only angry lovers know.
They share in our deep devotion, maybe once or twice a year.
I long to once again taste your storing malice.

Introspection

George Major

This Journey's Too Sweet to Miss

I challenged my mind one evening, thinking in doom
my rivers flowed wide.

I fought repression, political nightmare, suppression of
love and anger and came out fighting
with a name I call, "The Sweet Fight."

I've discovered faith, the deepest kind with color and
vision.

A firm believer in truth and the depth of honesty to the
world travels with me.

I stand naked and alone to the window of the soul and
search out brevity and lonely people
bringing them back to life with hope.

The loneliness of a village mind stretches from the
depths of hell,
not wishing,
to the puritanical luster of heaven.

I've even been to India on the wing of genius and seen
the epic Mahavira,
the Buddha,
mantras and meditation propose a change of venue for
my soul.

I will abide in the recesses of heaven with God and
humor,

I have not given up my soul to the swamped
motherland India proposes, there's deep mires
There's something I wish to expose in due time, with
research, personal discovery and lunar landings.

Life is so deep, rich and vast.

The path of a believer, the faith of a poet to each day
verse a line such notions leave me in the clefts of anger
at why I had not discovered true love so soon.

I've seen Negroes become kings and cry at hazes and
port holes,
drifting in the wind,
my Negroes I have a right to know and will never give
up my behaviour toward the world.

I've seen streams of gold, rivers of blood, little
children split through the night
by tigers
and recovered in the morning with a joyous mood to
write lines in faith,

Giving notions to the world that life is free of malice,
truly free if you believe, God numbs you
to pain and carries souls through horror for a purpose.

I've seen archipelago men, isolated in the back of the
world with bright shiny faces deliver to presidents
and Arkansas angels brief the world about the truth of
love,
rising higher and higher

than princesses in troubled lands and historical figures
who gave us purpose in the
sugar cane fields of this land.

I've seen Harries drift like fallen angels defying God
and giving me an ear to see if I was
listening to myself.

I will not trouble God for any purpose.

I've walked with God and angels, saw briefs on heaven
and sucked up on the pittances of
strangers going straight for the jugular
in conversation,
cutting clearly to the crux of the matter, social pride
and politics are heretics to islanders.

I have cried a sweet cry for heaven and saw the Africa
in the east rise to the pinnacle of my own country,
poor Africa carrying a challenge to the world.

This is topsy turvy, this is malady Malay but sweet.

I have sucked the bones and marrow with hidden tribes
deep within the jungle
too brave
to show the world who's watching.

I've hacked at midnight and been around for years
researching my mind gathering revision
and gathering hope, hope for the world.

I've seen treasures of enormous magnitude and bled
within for failure to deliver strangers and
midnight girls to my bed for more hallow life.

I gave an epic to a gentle she and she ran off with a
light man to the far reaches of the north.

I've longed to love like Jesus and I may get my chance
with some divine believer meeting me
so sweet to call me love on the line of neverary, sweet
Ramonia.

I've longed for goblets to give, gave away my essence
and drifted off into paradise
so many times
I've forgotten the world existed and brought back by
fancy strangers delivering my
name to a waiting ear miles, centuries away.

I jump for joy at the sight of going home.

The Rocks of Africa are heavy, they carry heavy
purpose, no fame and fortune cadences
here, the weight of strangers upon my shoulders are
heavy.

I will deliver prize or hope I never lived long Harpo.

I've seen you cry, and tasted your magical race and
lived not to confine myself
in people,
the world so vast demands more of us.

This midnight magic too sharp to hold a race together, this spinning world demands me
everywhere, my time is short and I am limited in resources by thinking.

I wander out with princes and travel back on my mind to the Irish moors,
I have ties there too.

Long principles, the hair, that magnificent hair that streams from lovers
like India's trail
leaves funk on the minds of young boys.

Kisses, generation's kisses, and sucking women leave a mind to see the world.

I lusted long time ago and came out with every race imaginable, I'm a mixed race season
with a wish
to travel the world in the hearts of many seeking my loveliness in verse.

I wish for the masses and see the candid humor on white faces and live to tell stories to
strangers sitting in the lap of luxury and give it all away for more.

This stream, this deep river is never-ending.

I saw a rainbow yesterday and did a dance in New York, slow dance to death and was

delivered at midnight upon a bench and saw myself the
loneliest man in history,
a lonely dying man
with a wish to encircle the world with this heart of
Jesus, so vivid, such delusion.

I present this murky enterprise to heaven to make me
up this wish that I see the world and
brace my will to quiver in love alone with Ramonia.

I lock my vices to history, give up all my quests and
golden wishes for a chance at history.

I wish for love and grimace with the hope that in a
foreign from the heart of the matter, the crux of me,
this lonely paradise harbor, I find love in the recesses.

I pray my life with hope and give up magnets and long
for dropping sticks.

Some masters of life may hear my cry and know the
brevity of my desire.

I pray for exclusion from the pain of death and long to
live forever in a vast heaven
with love,
eternal love first for my master of life, God, his onlys,
and love for Ramonia.

I am here with purpose, adrift with all my gaze, rich
with vision, the scope of generosity like
the depth of my soul, I've known no other gift.

I throw this all away for one wish, my love for
Ramonia live.

Sing for me sonique, the drifts of angels make me cry
in delight that I knew your age.

The deepness of my soul goes out to you all of Africa,

I hear the hearts of many get out, I wish for my flavor
and know one day I get my chance in heaven
with believers wishing us home.

Sing for love, give it all for love, I hear you angel.

The roundness of your tone touches me deeply,
sweetness clarity, divine love for masses of heart,
prompt colors giving up never hearts afloat on a
magical world of mixture.

I long for this love and cry my heart out in vain.

Someday I might know the pimples and grandeur of
reflection.

God knows I've longed for hearts and gotten a
collection on the air.

Angels like my Mayas, the childish views and busty
lips of hope, the midnight magical
gleam of Toni's and Terrie's and the bastard sons of
the eastern treasure I hold too near my heart, I've seen
their golden hair, spinning black gold.

I've seen this lusty enterprise for too long and not wondered from whence my mother came.

The craft, this journey too sweet to deliver me.

I will ask to never give up this plight to reunite people, people with love and vision and depth and discipline, like behaviour and purpose so strong.

Looking in the eyes is not seeing the love of humans, that was my first clue.
Looking in the soul brought me home, giving my soul to a child gave me up a clue and giving up my life to the Saviour of life for guidance the true belief, the true hope that one day we all may get to heaven.

How might I live not for myself but for the world?

Who gave me this fortune that I may sit with hearts and pleasures, platting baskets, running on the beach, giving time to dreamers, who would have thought that this was my way, my glimpse of heaven here on earth.

Make me cry more for heaven when this day has ended.

Let me see the epics and people calling out to the world, some day give us a happy
meeting.

A meeting of the minds like Frost and Chaucer, Beckett, the angry pockets of Salman, the wishes in a dreamer from the isolate west in Derek of St. Lucia fame, nobleman firm believer with a grip on the future of the races.

Split, conquer and divide, get the message out.

Leave the lily livered wash alone, you are not confined to anger, you can love and forgive as Christ gave us hope.

Give up wine women and song and know the strength of the world you are in.

Learn to spin magic in ears and see maidens cry in delivery of your discovery of hearts.

I have tasted this milk and long for this passion forever.

Leave me alone with this world for I am resigned for fight, for love forever giving no
misconception for my deeds.

I am wild with faith and growing daily with belief.

I wish to strive with you, the world in our uni-collective fight.

I cry out from my perch, this heavenly nightmare will not end with tomorrow.

I make my way to heaven daily and make derision my prize, my daily delight

and pen verses
in perception, affecting homes powerful belief and if I
fail forgive me I was wrong a stranger.

If I fail to deliver your direction your true purpose call
me out and gave me some inkling of tame,
I'll need a wish for tomorrow.

I see my plight ending with the golden gates, a tremble
and a wish in hand
I'll enter
And briefly speak with God and try for deliverance
home.

Death too wild and common, spoken of the breath like
mint in a daily mouth.

I call out to you all for deliverance, deliver me in mind,
give your hearts out in possession of trust.

I hope for you, you hope for me.

As Henri sits in Cuba alert in minds and hearing
forgiveness on the breath of babes.

Paz Fuera, peace out to the world, a grand collection of
souls adrift dreaming for a reach to heaven,
father hear our prays, even on the breath of strangers
common visions, heaven.

This journey too sweet to end.

George Major

Fears of our Fathers

Young men!
The fears of our fathers drive us
his social and political rage
his misguided reckless desires
his follies may freely engage,

Our fathers' ideas inside us
we move on from day to day
That deep hurting cloak
that will guide us to hell
when it has its way.

How can we live with this
other seeming side.
When our life is locked deep inside us.
The life that teaches us to hide.

To flee the angry bastards
so openly filled with rage.
Pacing at a distance the keeper
of us and our cage.

This angry nightmare
plays on from day to day,
not knowing when to wake up,
not knowing what to say.
When all our passion guides us we slowly take a stand,
our hopes in someday knowing this son will be a man.

Streams of gold

Just before the dawn I arise
Sugarplums in heads imagining the truth will come
forth, the greatest creation of all today.
I arose this morning to find that I was cold.
The night before had only given me the misery of
closed eyelids and peace till dawn.

I dress myself for the purpose and see myself in a
warm winter neck-piece, green.
The winds of March are upon us and they will prevail
'til whenever.
It is a morning to be seen in application of work.
Not to disguise and give up the effort.

I had promised at least one golden spoon a day.
That is what I was about to give, on golden doubloon.
This effort for their purpose and mine.
We can work collectively with purpose.

Some how it works out fine at Christmas each working
on their own together bringing out the beauty of the
entire town.
It had to work here as well.
I'm not the only one who can decorate.
I'm not the only one with words and an imagination,
An ear open to the outside world.

So on we go looking for golden doubloons, golden
spoons spun in a magic sky.
This morning we would see gold.

Just beyond the horizon streaks pinkish orangey glaze in the winter sky clouds adrift give no clue of the coming features of the morning,
Cold and black they hang forever moving slightly over the light blue plain like high planes drifters belonging there.
There's some rain in sight.

Below the black masses of the clouds lies the forever-green hue of the forest.
No doubt there's some pigeon plums out there in the distance, I haven't had those since I was a child.
I could rediscover that anytime I think.

The sky grows wilder as the brightness opens up enough to see that something is coming over the horizon.
Who knows how today will be.
I just celebrated with a prayer to the Almighty of the Ages, he understands me well.
He sends me timing and nightmares alike to keep my imagination wild and filled with promise for poetry and wild writing interludes.
Isn't it wonderful to know almost every aspect of the world and what a common day will bring?

Bring everything besides tragedy I am told to make believe.
Tragedy transcends our understanding of the world.
We never knew why it came.
The purpose of tragedy is to move the victim's friends and family into devout action, get tighter with promise and deliver, he says from above.

No room for slack behaviour, these days no room for smiles.
Just light humor for the bereaved, don't loose your sense of humor or all is lost in a maze.
Humor is the key to many things and why they happen.
He teaches us that through experience.

Don't be afraid to laugh at yourself you know.
Funny things happen when I'm not around and no one else is near so have humor with yourself and know why, you need it.
It's essential for life you know.
And life must go on no matter what happens, even I know that.

So the skies are opening, the rays are getting warmer, not present directly just bright shadows in the distant sky reflect the coming of the sun on a winter morning like this.
I'll await the warming of the earth this morning, it's cold out here.
Clad sweater, green with a turtleneck I punch out a line, a golden doubloon soon stretched out of the imagination, cool ingot ready to be discovered by the world.

Ah! On further observation the clouds carry their reflection high on top.
The golden bright delivery must be the real thing, the coming of the sun direct without bouncing mirrors to behold.

I'm in love with the sun on winter days, I know too well what it brings, too many things to recollect in one line so I'll play here the muse.
The warming touch is gleaming in the tops of the clouds.

Accompanied by the rustle of God in the evergreen trees, the sunlight coupled with this is the coming of magic in the morning.
A grand enterprise to witness and not forget in summer when too much sun is near.
It's still a miracle that all this is ours on any day in the world.
I am told the earth is forever, I don't know, I just know that I'll have my days with God anywhere, his promises never cease.
I won't get heady with logic, clever with disguised wisdom, I just said it plain, the kind of love that enough to know anytime.

Wow, here she comes, the golden rays of sunlight, and do you know the clouds are vaporized, just up and disappeared.
The skies are thin and clear.
The bright golden rays in the distance over the horizon have vaporized but a few clouds leaving a grand aqua blue canvas to cover the sky.
Now it drops touching the green waking trees, jostling in delight this morning has broken beyond the horizon the sunlight glares, golden with a purpose, the day is open and new.
A time to rejoice, another winter's day is near,
If I sound too excited I'm happy.

My mother's gone and I have a neck to believe in the dawn of sunshine as magic from heaven.

I feel so alive and warm.

The new day of promise has begun a midst our modern dream.

Just as it had centuries ago when Columbus sailed indirectly to our shores.

I am alive with golden hue, a wonderful golden doubloon to spend in the hours of the day.

One ingot of mystery to enjoy for the waking hours of the moment.

One day will not last forever so now I will go, just now the surface popped out above the horizon the full force of the sun is coming upon us, I can see the golden streams on the trees above the skies, the direct thing skipping and shadowed gold into my eyes.

Not the full intensity just masked by vapor to know the fullness there of.

An example of the power of His majesty vacating near us to remember the days when images are down.

Look up and see the certain power of His majesty.

One day a man from Holland told me, "I do not believe in God, he does not exist, this is our eastern belief, agnosticism."

I soon after some time discovered who that man was, God himself on a test of myself and my belief.

Don't stop believing in the miracles you see.

Wake with the sunrise in the east and renew your faith in God every morning.

George Major

Paz Fuera, solo mente mi.

Quelled into contentment

Quelled into contentment like some quiet under prize.
The working mind goes weary from discovering the gloom.
That life had cheated me at 37 when I found my mystery out certain.
I had not pressured well enough to grow at an alarming pace while young.

Young men knew more than I.
I didn't know why or how but discovered through adversity that I had been left upon the shelf to dry.
There were young doctors at twenty-four who bring about the best knowledge in the world.
But not to despair, I'm getting my share of easy life.

Life after discovering what pressure tremendous excitement brings, holding back on delight carries with it a prize.
Mine was stolen from me, cheated in an eternal affair by the wrong suggestion was my fate.
Some jumper in disguise got around to me early and cheated me out of life well.
I'm not angry, mother keeps the kettle on and quells all my fears with medicine into contentment.

I am given women as discovery makes its way in form.
Beautiful, lonely choices which one of which will be mine is not a toss up.

Sweet Ramonia wins the prize hands down with her delight and glowing ways toward a heaven I know so well.

I will go on the morrow as soon as issues are resolved and lay with her in contentment, quelled into contentment is not as bad as it seems.

Fascination

Fascination begins with attention by sight, by sound, by feel.

One begins, his gaze open to style, he the beholder opens his heart to the temptation in view.

Fascination goes only so far. By gazing, feeling, sounding, perceptions are changed and brought into view.

How far then does fascination go?

Fascination is not depth, its limitations you ask? It's only a surface view.

Try fascination and beyond, there's something more to bite.

Here, there's more depth, more perception, more by which to feel and gaze, sound and see.

I'm fascinated by a smile, that curious grin.

We see that smile, exposure of dental digits, a spider's view it is the interior of the mind.

Yet, fascination ends, so quickly it ends.

You see, admire, sound and gaze.

Just then that sight so luring engages and fills your passions envy.

Then fascination is at its end.

Then on to the next, that fancy of mind that glitters, encapsulates and binds attention.

Thus lending itself as another fulfillment in an otherwise dull, daily task.

George Major

All is Quiet on the Western Front

All is quiet on the western front.
Just fog over yonder hills.
See what souls are like today
They may be genuine in nature, or filled with too much
pride.

These days one never knows the enemy.
All are bright with impish smiles and mastery of voice.
How can I tell the truth from the norm.
Bull shit, someone said over the balcony, shut up and
address us in the afternoon.

How can I stroll in forbidden territory with a million
dollars on my head?
Relax the samples near ending, relax there's no more
else to prove.
Be a brave fighter and see the miracles rise out of the
earth.
One in a minute at a time, we have the power to prove
this solidity.

I hope to see you among the lions of the day, she says.
The timidness I feel inside knows no end.
Although I am among the brothers, they hold the key
to life if they have not missed the mark.
We all tremble with fear at the notion that all this glory
may be over.

The wicked are nearly out.

We've proven this method of shepherd-ship holds evil
at bay,
evens out a village pride and makes bitter meat of
calamity air.
Sunshine or miracles you choose to be the same.

Most are up with the sunlight morning.
The eerie coolness of the morning carries with it a dose
and promise.
This day, that I am here no less, will bring with it the
fruits of labour.
The early hours in preparation say so.

No doubt that the baskets in the fields will see some
abundance,
No doubt that the master craftsman on the waters will
have a day to match yesterday's offerings.
Prepare for village life.
Work a day, work as hard as you know and let them
out in the shadowy bright sunlight of the evening.

Position yourself on a rock, stabilize that fear of
knowing, see Jesus his ghost, the father nigh climb
around the mental world.
Carrying with them the promises made a hundred years
ago, this paradise is yours forever, no calamity in that.
Just life everlasting, turnips, garlic, curries, peppers
and don't forget vanilla, all apart of the rendering and
the promise.
Comfortable strangers bring on vitality, fervor, juice
for marrowed bones longing for enterprise.

The beautiful smiles contained in strangers faces, the lightness of purpose and the ease of character.

Come to me like my woman in the night, feel my passion, my temperature down, a tickle might do the trick.

Already I love the air of the afternoon where happy strangers walk carrying packages, candy delights.

Strangers need no invitation to smile and walk among the natives, we accept our homage and love every minute, it works.

Maybe a glistening quarter of an hour may pass before one catches the will to live for the next, no more than a quarter.

Checked and chartered by the voice of the ages one must go forward with delight and measure the time at hand.

Have you finished that most important work of the ages?

The one just a minute ago, I told you it's the most important in your life, finish that work and be prepared to go to heaven.

This is the miracle of life, one never knows.

Every minute the nightmare of calamity is at hand, alive and fresh, fight for a miracle.

Village life and people are not the most comfortable assertion one has but they are genuine, purposeful at least not worried

And doggish like many in the world.

Anyone loves a people striving for heaven.

Get off the conviction, release the energy of mind and feel the fantasy rise from within, miracles never cease.

Our happiness with the lord I'm told, the local lord, villager zero on the top disciplinary plane.
That man has tenacity.
He tells me dreams, he tells me dreams like I've never known, making my passion rise with tickles and knobs, like lolly-winks and candy delights, a joyous afternoon may be mine to lie and wait for a lover's wish while lobster teaming at the mouth of caves beneath the crimson sea line in droves for my masters to procure, wanted definition there it is.
More of the mastery of village life.

I'm never saw such prudence, such careful meditation
I've always known miracles to match nature's naked enterprise.
Raped at seventeen I saw the vision intended for my kind.
Never had university but I talk with presidents of college so wide and varied it'll make a midnight dream end.

The best of them come to me for juicy marrow, stain and life.
I give it all with happiness and pride, this life is never ending, the joys procured for the living, how to help the dead is knowing.
Rotten bones, settled sediment, locked inside a cavernous cave, let's go for a walk hold my hand I'm grave.
Shuddering with excitement, that moment of bereavement carries far to tell this villagers life.

I hear; don't chase me out, I've nothing to prove, I'm here in meditation with the living, my rock knows the harbor well even at his age.

The golden rising sun, cool, wafting air like puffy sugar crisps, one needs a reminder to breathe.
The excitement gathered around this market, so lively with fish leaves much still to the imagination.
Red turtle beef in the distance, walk over calmly and see the red glistening creature give up its life in a pop and surge, off to heaven with pride, turtle is a warm delightful texture, a seismic vibration to the old factory, a genuine catch for hobby fishermen without a promise or a day's work all in a village harbor.

Life unending, here everyday, the village trough, feeding ground for many wishing to see the fogginess of mind go out.
Public calamity, genuine humor and people filled with secret purses, slipping dollars and dimes up palaces; I know what's going on.
Jah vibrations booming in a quiet corner of the market some raspy soldier needs a way out of meditation.
Why tell me so I cannot tell.
Mista' im say, can I get a lift on a target live for a century or more?
In they come looking for a chance to stay and live through local examples, maybe a few may enter, just a few.
Life is too fragile in a village to balance permanent strangers never ending influx of ideas, dangerous.
Leave the village, live and know that many hearts draw the same ideology, the same drawing of the cards.

No perky ideas permitted, nothing out of the ordinary, non-surprised, no relative nightmares to shock the masses, just humor and candid approach, village lives are precious, just as any other is.

Be gentle and walk among the divine creature with open hearts so soft and warm, pluming with genuinity.

We're true to the world, give us our needs, our daily bread and several strange hearts to warm, assurance for tomorrow in this

Beautiful garden and our life is yours forever.

This our prayer goes out to the world, humble souls on barriers, adrift with the lonely mannerisms of decades of village life.

We love it here, we intend to stay until the market closes.

Push us not, for miracles never cease,

Delight and pleasure abound in life in a village by the sea which nature brought our way through Columbus, Isabella, Bermuda religious sects, the African hardness we know so well.

All these combined over the decades to build a centuries pleasure, work everyday work never alone.

Jah bless miracles.

Paz fuera

George Major

Out of nothing comes nothing

Take a blank piece of paper, what is there?
Nothing worth mentioning.
Now take that sheet of paper and give it to Andy
Worhal
At least you'll get back something weird, an idea, a
promise for the knowing.

From nothing comes nothing.
There is nothing in a lost promise except grief.
Take a piece of paper naked and white prepare it well
with an imagination.
Jot down your thoughts and see the color taking shape.

You can see that there is something in this simple
notion.
Colors, imagery are from the imagination, endless
ideas powerful enough to change the world.
But before you do so make sure to prepare the paper
with imagination somewhat filled with sugarplums.
We want something good not another goulash
nightmare about the cemetery.

Have the power to move us, with our language.
Use our perceptions and thoughts to create something
new in the way of ideas.
Something we have not heard before.
Even a century ago poets opened up their mind with
the notion of filling the canvas with the last epitaph of
enlightenment.

They haven't succeeded yet, there's so much more to write.

Edgar Allan Poe had the idea some macabre bent notions.
Give us better than that nothing deranged something of a Derek Scott, not nearly an Emily Dickenson but light and refreshing
Like snow on a summer's day has the tendency to melt the hearts of many.
There's gold there in the Caribbean something for someone to mine, mine this notion you'll be great and as famous as you ever imagined

Think up sonnets, lines of meter, refrain and suspend the public by reading your magic.
Lit the pages with excitement and energy like no other poet has done yet.
Keep your mind and heart open to imagination like no other muse this century.
They will praise you poet with delight with what you have given them has no equal beyond and in the imagination you are impassable.
Someone will try but they will praise you with a century's notions.
You the prize winner of the hour will win your heart's enchantment enough magic to keep a woman warm for a century and beyond.
Why beyond? Because life goes on forever, clever imaginations know it, why don't you?
You're the poet or perhaps you choose not to remember to caught up in your own tragic nightmare.

Just give us the lines you promised when you thought this dream would end soon.

Our souls will be here tomorrow and the next day.

Wear yourself with writing clever lines, suspending, speeding, pushing imagination to its limits.

I'll thank you when I feel my brain move with pleasure.

Squeeze the juice to one side and feel forever slipping out for a minute.

The tentacles glazed, black and grooming, sucking back life as they contract back below the surface.

Like an alien trapped inside a great body of poetry juices, you get the notion, that's the picture I wish to portray.

I'm scared sometimes and don't know where to turn, the creature inside me might get angry and spin me out of purpose.

What am I to do then? Go crazy without a friend to rely on.

My sponge brain knows enough lines now to sustain itself for days.

I have enough entertainment to be wrapped in a grave forever if today was the last day.

I know how to get out secretly and see the world through imagination and in candor.

I have imagined these tyrannical nightmares and I can't be far off from wrong.

The sonnets resonate in my mind like chalices before and ancient princess, which to choose.

Choose the juicy fat one that near got out to the world, it'll be our secret.

You cannot pay me for this anymore, I am beyond money.

Beyond the sonnet's prize am I.

I am drilling for a notion, probably another half hour will leave me with enough anxiety to go back to the real world and wait for a miracle to happen.

For now this brief moment we share together friend I will search the corners and find the notion that you love.

Come back to me on a summer's night when we can walk along the ocean and take a moonlit stroll along the winding white beaches I have reserved for the rich, maybe in doing so you'll discover me and pull me out of my shell for a while.

We can know the magic of live on an isolated island of paradise and archipelago forever.

Tell me are you willing to walk?

Its only a matter of notion, trim bodies wafe, no ties to another besides me the man you're with and we could have eternity on a beach, maybe even make a soul together in time.

I have the notion you have the fresh pluming flower, the delight a holy man seeks after in age gone too far.

Let this holy man bereave at your feet if you are not the one.

My imagination is open, delivering me from the caves we dwelled in before.

I want to live in paradise for sure, although I have no money to speak of.

The best things in life are free, if only you see them with honesty and an open heart.

Come share with me, the ample breast of time so far
from nothing else to lie on, I call on thee.

You may be the one to occupy this notion I carry of
mother's milk when babies crying give way to another
suckle breast-burdened man.

Should I be ashamed to suckle mother's milk from the
willing?

I do not know that answer to mother's milk, I only
know the notion and will get there when the time
comes.

Trust for now the melody you hear.

I didn't hear the crickets today, I heard the rushing of
the wind, God is closer today, his roaring imagination
ahead of my own.

I've heard his sonnet and opened up my heart to his
belief and promise, hear what he says, "If only you
believe in me."

And so I do, I'll have my place in paradise if I am
careful not to spill the prize over the floor.

Keep it, the prize, with a notion to make more.

A soul of enlightenment like you to honor me forever
in paradise, such a mixture of humanity.

This is what God said to me one day, he gave me this,
do you believe me? You must!

Without deception I have been close to God, several
times he has tugged on my heart and made me feel the
notion to go home.

I have said that I will, but why go home to an empty
house, there must be children playing in the
background, the notion of milk and honey hit home the
next day, just a figure of speech I'd imagine.

Meat is the substance for an Island man like me.

Tell me now if you will come, just to walk with me my light frame and face appearing naked to the wind like yours is pure magic to my heart.

You're the Boganskia dream I cannot release, you are centuries old already.

I have traveled worlds away, catching up with the glorious earth that is your home.

I will never give up chase over you.

If not this life, Boganskia, the next.

I wish to love you near, touch your tender heart and feel your delight jiggle inside while weeping at thee the holy grail of my imagination.

Next to God you are it for me, my reclamation prize, my envy for my life, and with that sometimes I am selfish and will let you know when the memory of you is too much for me to bear.

I can feel no other life but this and I must know the world belonging only to you and I.

We can live together, produce sonnets, with meter and rhyme, humorous and delightful as life must be.

Today I have carried with me the imagination I wish for thee.

Open up your mind and see that I love you like no other.

I will go to the other woman out of necessity but my Boganskia prize you are the magic of the ages.

Though I never had you, I've tasted your milk, saw your garden in my imagination, the brownness of grasses unfurled beneath the cold canvas covered up in the warmth, let's sup, can I draw you in?

Yellow eyes like miracles, let me fantasize on the notion not for long but for long enough to tingle.

I've seen our treasure that's enough for me, yet still I want more.

I claim you for the ages and will not forget, my Boganskia, yellow light eyes and tight wired lips making it a glimpse like a tigress in heat.

Just curious not intruding, enough to arouse even the heaviest of men.

You're the one Boganskia my life without God in mind first is for you.

Now to re-coin a phrase, this light imagination is great.

Take that piece of white paper write me a sonnet from which I cannot refrain.

You know my mystery,

You've been there before where you can have it all in one minute or keep it all for a century or more, you know my dilemma you've seen me before.

Catch up to me and write me something, cherish the thought to notice me while with naked imagination.

You've undressed me with your eyes, I know.

I'm the envy of many men this century.

I hope to live on forever, if not present here then with the Lord in heaven.

Write sonnets, chase magic and know the answer to the great riddles so many of them in the world.

Work them out with your mind, it's simple if you have the knack for the notion.

Even Boganskia's mystery I know, I've chased that dream for too long.

I'm off now to forever, back to centuries jump, not a night of more elusive magic but a night of peace through pills, sweet illuminated notions and pills.

Buenos nochas, I'll see you on another summer's day when God is rustling through the trees and brightening the horizon.

Much love and leisure, rest with the one who matters most in your heart.

I will rest with thee, give me the notion…

George Major

Operating Velocity

Any time you're in a hurry you know something can
go wrong.
Staring at the page you know that nothing will go right
for you today.
Damaged nerves are the answer to your search, your
assistance weaned and deserted.
But that's not the poetry head, that's the attrition.
People just don't stick in times of crisis.

You reach a crisis a day.
Certainly you call it a crisis when you're in a crowd of
people and cannot speak.
Awaiting answers to your everyday work-about life.
How did you suspect there'd be a miracle in this?
Pontius Pilot had his slaves so long ago.
You have yours by the mind, captive to your wings,
giving you the gravy, the good stuff indeed.

Keep your mind open to the world and see the magic
drift in line by line,
Elegant maze.
Nothing comes to weepers, the confident know the
wean, give in to your despair,
You're probably right if you imagined it.
No illusions here, tongues on snakes shiver through the
mind entrapment in a conscious decision,
You're held captive and you don't know who did it.

The conscious mind knows faith, fate's other half, the
conscious one, considerate of others.

Parity in a frenzy, hurry up on a group of strangers in the village and see how this works.

Someone got a line to you and you don't know who it is.

A gift from the living, generous souls who prefer to live in a nightmare world for solace and supplication.

Do share the grandeur of the promise, they'd like to know who's up in the morning so as to catch up on the know.

The charmer, the delight wormer new to this enterprise, shock value you see.

Gentle humor to talk of fucking on a summer's eve.

Surprise matches delight when fresh angel meat enters the fold, don't be alarmed be cool and see the tremors aligned within.

This is the way to fancy, this is the way of the world, thank God I'm here.

My head is clear, the nightmare over, perhaps for a while, who do you identify with, Gucci or Gandhi?

The better soldier of the modern age, you might try Gandhi G.

His impact on the world self evident of a miracle man, miracles move he world now, not leather bags and fancy attire,

Tie into the miracles, this may be the last effort, time of nigh are near.

This could be the last millennium, the apocalyptic end of the world.

Don't panic, play along, God is not in a hurry to crush the human spirit he believes in.

Altered attention, given through miracle mazes tell me
that God is a brother, humorous and on our side.
Wait with the world for miracles never cease.

Heavy Drifts

Heavy drifts come over me at times.
Why I had not discovered the world much earlier is my
refrain.
There's so much to know, how do they know it all.
I go on memory.

I shiver at the notion that I have not gotten it well.
Perhaps I lack faith.
Do they go on memory or does it stream at times of
needing.
Once ago I wanted to cover the whole mystery of debt
before I was married fair.

I thought that was the right approach.
It didn't work,
Still panic stricken from debt and riddled with more
mysteries to attain,
I have to go on forward and die with the others in a life
filled with questions and the unknown.

Not some comfortable affordable nightmare but a
public shared with millions not hundreds, a public
nightmare indeed.
You have to be perfect in that world or be found out to
be in error of life.
What a shameful discovery.
Admit it your just like the rest, I know but I won't give
in.

God has given me the gift now of gentle mastery,

I quiver not when faced with angry promise.
Somehow God works it all out for me.
In this short life of days, I haven't gone hungry for delight yet.

I'm a miracle prize, anyone in my possession gets a charmer with an enviable disposition.
The ability to love without end is mine.
I can love the best out of need.
Give love and need love I say.

Imagine with the mind that she loves you well and that you won't give up ever for her sake.
Keep her in mind with your discoveries.
I wish I could give her everything.
I'm working on that so hard.

Love comes to believers, we fell into love so strong.
She believes my mind and that I love her now forever.
I'll grow into it too, it tingles me when I hear her exclaim that, "I love you, baby."
Such a gentle wind prevails in that exclamation.

It's so easy to be good with the world after such a lucky day of fate.
You're in love for the sake of being in love.
Sight unseen except through photos and still you're in love.
How circular, how divine.

If she matches my nightmare when we meet, I'll be a perfect man.
I'll find her everything she needs to be the one for me.

I'll love her until the pots turn black with envy and I'll clean those daily.
I'll love her well.

Well enough to see spires rise to the sky.
Imaginary but true spires which I can climb making a difficult stairway to heaven.
I believe in heaven so strong.
It can take us both to that eternal nirvana now that we love each other so strong

Sweet Ramonia, I wish that you were near now.
I'd weep with you, your breasts so wide with fury and magic, soft delightful magic.

George Major

Why God Made Me a Poet

Because stories and people need telling is why.
Because I walk with angels on gossamer wings of truth
and need deliverance in faith is why.
When I reach abreast the milestone where he wants me
to be I stride and process the word for the world.
I sit aloft bound by passion and mystery of purpose
and write delightful notions for the masses to see.

That they will see the divine creator in me is why.
When I write my mind is open to divinity.
In creeps the ghosts of ages and clears the pathway for
something new each day.
Because the world needs reminding of his divine
purpose through words unexplained.

He is a God of mystery as well as fulfillment.
God gives us mysteries to open up the way of trust.
Lust not with the angels and know not shame, just
enough to make you willful and acceptable to the
masses, then we can live together without anger.
Here is our word for today, make light of divinity at
times, know the lasting nature of humor in the divine.

God is in everything you can imagine, see him there.
He will talk to you if you search him out enough.
He is not an angry God, give him your measure of faith
and he will reveal himself to you in time.
No need to hurry, he has given us eternity in his arms,
to them that do believe.

His majesty and miracles are claimed and exclaimed daily for those who search him out.

Divinity is my purpose eventually I strive with this in mind.

Help me to remember everyday to look to his garden of the world for his authority in figures and people.

Search me out the truth that I may know he is going on and be reminded of his worth to my soul.

We are on a journey to forever with him lest we forget and miss the mark is why God made me a poet.

To bring the believer into focus of his art and ability to rock the world and lay even claim to the dirt is his majestic ways.

I feel that God is near.

Ever present and true, make me up this poem in memory of his belief, God I love your ways and am your divine creature in the world.

George Major

My Sense of Purpose

I feel a mastery here, a mastery of life no less undefined.
In carving out a niche I chose the most high.
The authority, the alchemy and mastery over all living things,
an undefined sense of purpose, this haze is driving me mad.
Though ghosts, gods and monsters gather around me pinching,
freezing clasps in the night, I feel nothing but calm.
Have I overcome the fear of the unknown?

I feel the light run through me with the thought of ghosts.
My mind running a clock and hour out of speed not out of control,
then I drift off to sleep and awaken wet with heaven's glaze
and wonder what wonde6al things might happen today.
Like the angels, in demure divine purpose, I tingle at the notion
that something may come my way.
I'm free to believe, and in that belief I share with others
less than a follicle away from my mystery.

Be it angels or masters there's something in the wind,
something to whom I must bind
to be a devout believer, a carrier of news connected
with the world in ecstasy no less doubtful, someday I

may get a wife to hallow my shape and seed some
fertile ground,
until then dreams and goo at night will do.
I'll let it run for as long as necessary until the right one
comes.
Thick in perdition the prize in night.
Threshing on the distant horizon and over the phone
she's ready for the mystery of my life.
Come and live with me, she says but not so fast for the
lonely one
may be sucked up into nothing.
I'll take my time and ensure the pudding will last till
dinner time.

I feel no brevity here.
No shortness of breath, just promise of prose and
words, divine telling unending.
So when does breath end, when words can tell no more
and life is at its end.
My life will last forever in the parchment of heaven.
I pray for that everyday.
That glorious prize that is my life, beyond almost
money I feet a plateau of necessary evil
that may be changed and forced upon me by the
master, a mystery I have yet to fulfill.
The need for money is a master in our lives today, all
of us.

So into guise we go undaunted by the light of day.
Not clever with dreams but wishing that life will go on
sweet and in serene quietude
until we get our piece of the prize.

Just imagine for a while that life today might be that piece.

This day on heaven's earth might be that prize and go further than that.

I feel that way and know that possibility.

I must settle and be free and honest with the master of life.

An awesome responsibility.

How to keep my heart open to questions to which I know no answer.

The devil may slip in occasionally causing me to lie.

Not matching his wit, how am I responsible for these?

Therefore I must go to heaven.

In my knowledge the fact that I believe in one divine God

as master and surveyor of all the earth and humanity is the answer to my faith.

I even believe in the comfort of maggots and flies now I'm so strong

in the purpose of death and our 'link to the true divinity up in heaven.

Even maggots and flies have their place in the truth of the food chain.

So I will go on believing and telling the crowds on summer days

when the rays of golden light are high, this is the gift today from the master.

Take this and sit with me in community, let's have a laugh,

some light humor while we're at it, and sit together in reclamation of this natural prize.

Let's work if we have it and do what we will to make ourselves happy.

Not think too strong, not all the time, and relax.

This may be the formula for life.

A life so free and true that God knows it himself and gave it to me

so that I might give it to you.

So here I am, disseminate to me great truth that 1 too may be happy.

Tell me more, I wart to know more of the mystery of life and how it might end

and why it goes on.

I need to know the purpose of the sun and the magic of the days drifting one by one.

I just learned to live one day at a time, instead of years I had reserved in my mind.

I lost that all and now I am much more happy, programmed by this meter each day

and led in divinity each moment,

my heart not heavy and. worried but burdened by fellow men.

Knowing full well that someday Christ may come and when he comes,

I wish to be there no matter my condition.

Make me matter above all else I have done.

This is not my brain, I only use it.

It too has masters beyond myself that creep in and confuse my purpose.

If for me I'd stay by the Caribbean Sea all day and watch the notions and golden rays

master God in mind and fish by the water's edge and feed the notion of heaven

with golden Bennie Cakes and thoughts of Junkaroo at Christmas.
I hope that in going to heaven I don't go mad.
Not clutching too tight, I might a heaven miss?
No tightness, squeezing the evil out in time from the upper palace is the notion.
Constant delivery of information, truth no less honest interaction.
Let them know the desires of your heart and you will be fulfilled one day if not all.

Some one smiled on me twice the other day,
I felt so special.
Still shame from the encounter I feel such pride to have touched a heart or two
with my delivery of ooze.
Such divine pleasure is mine that I do not have to touch to feel the guise
in the notions of the world's inhabitants we are largely alike in our searches for the most high,
and why we have to search is our mystery.
Searching in brevity and piece a greater notion for the world to ponder.
Search me out and know the desire of my heart for every human being is love and peace,
a candy notion of sweet delight.
I wish they could finish fighting in the east but even that may have a purpose.
Still without knowing I must go on.

Let me feel your warmth tonight.
Come into my mind and know my beautiful caress.

I may wish to live with you forever in the garden of the divine should God have it so.
I feel love for you and soon may see your face.
Thank you, father, for the real.

Paz fuera todos...

George Major

Dreams

For Brittany

I sit here with delight, an accomplished morning.
My mind at ease at having produced my greatest work.
I am resigned to deliver to you some sweet inspiration
for your trek throughout the world.
You are given a gift so many of us desire but cannot
have, your appeal massive as with your bright pearlies
you pierce the hearts of many throughout the world
and beyond.

I have seen you now, render your traditional fare, sheer
melody mixed with delightful appearance and sense of
purpose and mind.
Stronger than yesterday is more than a memory but a
total impact on the minds of the heeding masses.
I am stronger than yesterday.
I understand the yearnings of the heart that sang that
rendition.
No near murky laughter but beautiful reprisal sifting
glances and mixtures with lips of pearl venturing far
beyond the flat media, captured by the minds of witty
old pirates with memories of yester-year.

Until now I knew nothing of your existence.
'Til now I have sought out in brevity some semblance,
some desiring image with which to place this yearning;
maybe this is not you I imagine.
My mind has since raced with excitement at the notion
that one day you may appear, some fancy light surprise
for the heart of a holy man in search of nirvana and
beyond.

George Major

Somehow, in some summer night's dream you may hear the beating of the mind at work in your favor.
Sometime when least expected our paths might meet.
Then in great surprise, perhaps the touch, light gentle fury envelope, a smiling gaze ensue, the fluttering heart of surprise mutter forward and utter words of innocence in an assuming phrase, "How do you do?"

Once in reprisal, and with assumption, a greatly pitched, "Hi" might follow.
I want to know, not for desire but for long endearing friendship.
The heart of a holy man rests with the notion of having touched the world with lightness and humility, maintaining a sense that he has not lost but gained through experience and discipline.

That you might know my heart, the beautiful, youthful, sensation, bent head bobbing in rendition of her song,

Brittany Spears.

Charlie, the Internet and Bob Marley

Zipping across the world on wiry wings.
Jutting from the Caribbean to Amsterdam in seconds
seems a fantastic notion.
What kind of heat may be generated at this velocity?
Wish I were an electron waiting in the wing for the trip
back and forth.

It's certain almost and sure to a degree, most of the
time the trip never fails.
Just seconds, sometimes milliseconds, to Washington
or Dallas.
Zipping through the wire, organized, traveling along
with millions.
Turning corners, setting record speeds as long as the
voltage in the line keeps up.

Like millionaire honey bees in a colony of billions
more,
Sheer delightful and ready to travel the story goes and
I myself see it almost everyday.
Connection through the raspy card to central control,
messengers dispersed en route to many centers
throughout the world.
The Internet is a miracle mile, a technical marvel.

Some say my friend Charlie is an electron; he worked
on the wires and disappeared in a haze one day on the
electronic lines.
We never heard from him again only in dreams, almost
a nightmare I had last summer some years ago.

Brother Charlie came down from heaven to fester with my tired mind for a while.

He did not speak, just showed up charged with positive atoms, bright golden glow, miniature in size but glowing as large as a ray of the sun.

Charlie is now a miracle miler; quick and traveling like a nightmare among hot wires.

As hot as knives cutting butter, banging with we, us few from the clad board school building sit beating out a rhythm to Bob Marley's, "Could you be loved."

Our gang's favorite song.

We sang these songs in school a relief from the regular learning process.

Beating on tables, cool in new shiny cloth, blue and white, red embroidery on empty pockets

with gleaming eyes and no sense of the future, we gathered each day and lost ourselves when we could in Bob Marley and Sting mostly, "Turn on the red light, Roxanne."

The biggest hits of the day still memorable on the mind.

We were close, so much we didn't know.

Mostly the fearless three, Charlie the other guy and me.

Could you be loved was the statement, we needed love and slept quietly on this refrain until we found the love we needed in the world.

I don't know if they found it, I didn't have the chance to ask, I never did find.

I'm still searching and haven't given up hope.

I know a strange love in Charlie and the other...

A sort of camaraderie established by close quarter living,

Another joined us and now he's gone, blanketed beneath the sea, stringy, long, wild wired he's certainly up in heaven with the crew.

I hope he finds Charlie some day and finds the chance to sit down and sing, bang on buckets of desktops to the tune, the classic Effort from Marley,

"Could you be loved."

Such grand times those days when boy's heads discovered the basics of women, the notion of love and devotion.

I had my share of love at the time.

Midnight kisses, the deluge of love in women's pleasure, they sucked me dry, down to the bone I gave it my all.

My devotion to beautiful women unmatched in the western hemisphere.

Charlie got married, moved to Freeport, although heard about I never saw him again before the accident on the wires.

Enough voltage, the right conditions one can be zapped into eternity in a second.

Charlie was turned into an electron.

He did promise in my dream to assist me whenever he could through the wires.

Perhaps that's why my search is so fast, Charlie sturdy soul as he is assisting my search, not afraid last time I saw him in my dreams…

George Major

About the Author

Mr. George Major is a product of the Tarpum Bay Public School Educational System, a graduate of Windermere High School. He holds an associate degree from Erie Community College in Buffalo, New York, and has attended college at Rochester Institute of Technology where he studied electrical engineering technology. Today Mr. Major is involved in an electronics company in Tarpum Bay, Majors Electronics, and is the owner of several rental real estate properties in the Bahamas. He is, as well, a freelance writer for various online magazines and Bahamian newspapers, and is involved in news reporting for his personal websites and several Bahamian websites and continues to write Eleutherian, Bahamian short stories, poetry, prose, and articles daily among his other civic contributions and duties.

in the United States